New MODULAR SCIENCE

for GCSE

HOMEWORK BOOK

Ann Fullick • Patrick Fullick • Martin Stirrup

Heinemann Educational Publishers,
a division of Reed Educational & Professional Publishing Ltd,
Halley Court, Jordan Hill, Oxford, OX2 8EJ
Heinemann is a registered trademark of Reed Educational & Professional Publishing Ltd

OXFORD MELBOURNE AUCKLAND
JOHANNESBURG BLANTYRE GABORONE
IBADAN PORTSMOUTH NH (USA) CHICAGO

First published 1998

ISBN 0 435 569988

02 01 00 99
10 9 8 7 6 5 4 3

Edited by Tim Jackson

Designed and typeset by 320 Design

Illustrated by Shelagh McNicholas, Maggie Brand and Kim Williams

Printed and bound in Great Britain by The Bath Press, Bath

Contents

How to use this book

This homework book is designed to help you learn all the science you need for your GCSE. The questions are arranged by module. If you work through them, as directed by your teacher, they will help you to:

- develop your ideas about the topic
- make key notes or diagrams to use when you revise
- practise solving science problems
- get information from tables, charts and graphs
- see how science affects you and your environment.

The questions are graded, starting with simple excercises and getting harder. Higher Tier material is clearly marked by the diamond-shaped question numbers. Your teacher will tell you which questions to try.

Most of the information you need will be on the page with the questions. The questions are to help you learn, not to catch you out.

The formulae you need for calculations are given. There are often examples, too, so you can see how they are used.

Remember: Don't be content just writing down an answer. Think carefully – does your answer make sense? Could you explain it to somebody else? As you do each question, you should: read, think, do, check – and finally understand! If you are still in doubt, ask your friends or your teacher, but make sure you try to work it out for yourself first.

1 Copy and complete the following sentences. Use the words below to fill the gaps.

sensitivity   seven   reproduce respiration   excrete   move

There are .... life processes common to all living organisms. They all need food, and release energy from the food by ....

All living organisms .... to get rid of waste and .... all or part of their body.

When organisms .... they make more of themselves, and these offspring grow to adult size.

Living organisms react to changes in their surroundings – they show ....

2 **a** Non-living things can be similar in some ways to living things. Copy and complete this table to show which of the seven life processes each thing carries out. The first one has been done for you.

Life process	Salmon	Concrete	Car	Pig
needs food	✓			
respires using oxygen	✓			
excretes	✓			
reproduces	✓			
grows	✓			
moves	✓			
is sensitive to surroundings	✓			

b What are the three biggest differences between a living organism and a car?

3 The diagram (at the top of the next column) shows two types of cell from the human body.

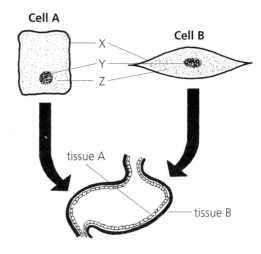

a Copy cell A and cell B and label parts X, Y and Z.
b What is the job of parts X, Y and Z?
c What type of cell is **i** cell A **ii** cell B?
d Tissues made of cells of types A and B work together in an organ known as the stomach. What is the job in the stomach of **i** tissue A **ii** tissue B?
e Which organ system is the stomach part of?

4

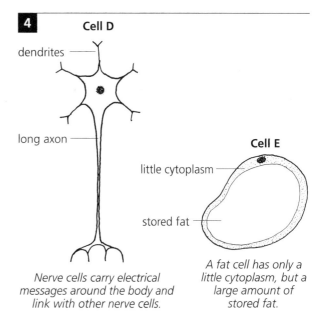

Nerve cells carry electrical messages around the body and link with other nerve cells.

A fat cell has only a little cytoplasm, but a large amount of stored fat.

Cells are often specialised to carry out a particular function (or job) in the body. Look at the diagrams of the cells labelled D and E and the description of their functions. Copy the diagram of each cell, and beside it make a list of the ways in which you think that its structure makes it particularly well suited to the job it has to do.

2 Healthy eating

1 Copy and complete the following sentences. Use the words below to fill the gaps.

carbohydrates   malnutrition   healthy
fats   energy   chemicals

It is important to eat the right amounts of food to remain fit and .... Food provides you with .... and the different .... you need to keep your body working properly.

The main types of food are .... , proteins and .... Eating too much, too little or the wrong sort of food can result in ....

2 Copy and complete the following sentences, choosing the correct ending in each case.

a Carbohydrates are found in food such as.....
b Both carbohydrate and fats supply energy.....
c Fats are found in food such as.....
d Too much, too little or the wrong sort of food.....
e Proteins, important for growth and replacing cells, are found in.....

Choose the endings from:
• .....cheese, butter and margarine.
• .....meat, fish, eggs and pulses.
• .....cereals, fruits and root vegetables.
• .....but the energy in the carbohydrates can be used more easily by the body.
• .....causes malnutrition.

3 Kelly made a note of the food she ate on a particular day.

• Breakfast: Rice Crispies with skimmed milk and sugar, cup of tea.
• Lunch: salad roll, cream bun, apple, water.
• Evening meal: chicken, chips, sweetcorn and peas, apple pie, lemonade.
• Snacks: chewing gum, bag of crisps, orange.

Copy and complete the table (at the top of the next column) for each of the foods Kelly ate. Some of the foods go in more than one place – for example, the cream bun would go under protein (the bun and the cream), carbohydrate (the flour and sugar in the bun) and fat (the cream)!

Carbohydrate	Protein	Fat

4 We get energy from all of the food we eat. But the balance of the different types of food we eat can affect our health – for example, we shouldn't get most of our energy from sweet things! The diagram shows the recommended amounts of energy an adult should get from the main types of food, including alcohol.

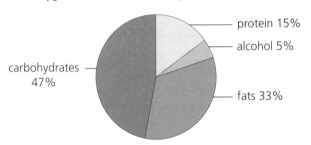

protein 15%
alcohol 5%
carbohydrates 47%
fats 33%

The figures given in the tables show the proportions of energy actually gained from the different types of food.

Men... Type of food	Amount of energy (%)
carbohydrates	44
protein	14
fats	35
alcohol	7
Women... Type of food	**Amount of energy (%)**
carbohydrates	45
protein	15
fats	37
alcohol	3

a Use the figures to draw a bar chart to show the proportions of energy actually gained from their food by men and women.
b Suggest reasons why the proportions are different for men and women.
c To meet the recommendations, most of us would need to alter our diets a bit. What sort of changes to the food we eat do you think would help us to get the right balance?

3 Cutting food down to size

1 Copy and complete the following sentences. Use the words below to fill the gaps.

mouth bloodstream enzymes digested gut digestive system

The food we eat cannot be used by the body until it has been broken down or .... This is the job of the .... Digestion begins in the .... and continues as food moves along the .... to other organs.

Special substances called .... are produced in your gut to help break down the food you eat into small, soluble molecules which can be absorbed into your ....

2

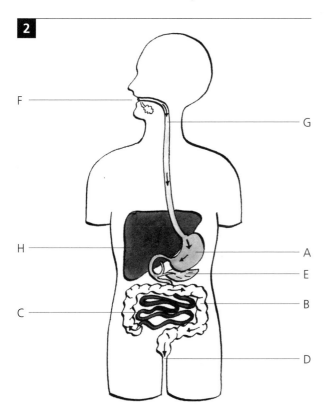

a Copy the diagram of the human gut. Use the labels below in place of the letters A–H on your diagram.
Mouth gullet stomach liver pancreas small intestine large intestine anus
b Write the function of that part of the gut next to each label.

3 People who eat diets rich in fibre produce lots of faeces and food passes through their guts in about 24 hours. People eating low fibre diets pass much smaller amounts of faeces and their food can be held up in the gut for several days. There is evidence linking the amount of fibre in the diet with the risk of developing cancer of the bowel.

Number of men aged 36-64 suffering from bowel cancer per year (per 100 000 men)

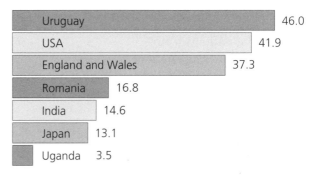

Uruguay			46.0
USA			41.9
England and Wales			37.3
Romania		16.8	
India		14.6	
Japan		13.1	
Uganda	3.5		

a In which two countries is bowel cancer most common?
b Produce a bar chart of the data from the table below showing the percentage of the food eaten in each country which is high in fibre.

Country	Percentage of food high in...		
	Fibre	Sugar	Protein
England and Wales	64	11	25
India	87	8	5
Japan	85	4	11
Romania	85	3	12
Uganda	95	2	3
Uruguay	67	8	27
USA	64	8	28

c Use the bar chart from part **b** to help you answer the following questions:
  i Which two countries eat most fibre-rich food?
  ii What is the incidence of bowel cancer in these countries?
  iii Which three countries eat least fibre-rich food?
  iv What is the incidence of bowel cancer in these countries?
d Do your bar charts support the idea of a link between fibre in the diet and bowel cancer?

3

1 Copy and complete the following sentences, choosing the correct ending in each case.

a A catalyst will speed up or slow down a reaction.....
b Living organisms make very efficient catalysts.....
c All enzymes are.....
d The reactions which keep you alive.....
e Digestive enzymes break down.....
f Each type of enzyme breaks down.....

Choose the endings from:
- .....could not occur without enzymes.
- .....made of protein.
- .....large food molecules into smaller ones.
- .....known as enzymes.
- .....a specific type of molecule.
- .....but is not changed itself.

2 Copy and complete this table to show the main digestive enzymes and what they do.

Name of the enzyme	What the enzyme works on	Products of digestion
protease	?	?
carbohydrase	?	glucose
?	fats	? and glycerol

3

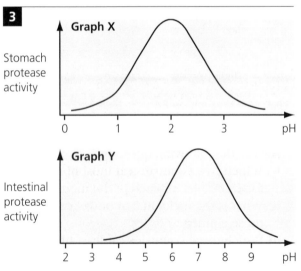

Graph X

Stomach protease activity

Graph Y

Intestinal protease activity

a Graph X shows the effect of pH on the activity of the protein-digesting enzyme produced in the stomach. At which pH does the enzyme work best?

b Graph Y (at the bottom of the previous column) shows the effect of pH on the activity of a protein-digesting enzyme from another part of the gut. At which pH does this enzyme work best?

c The acid conditions of the stomach have an important effect on bacteria which may be taken in with the food. What is this effect?

4 Some students investigated the breakdown of starch using the enzyme amylase (found in the saliva in your mouth). In one test tube they kept starch solution at room temperature. In the other two tubes they mixed the starch solution with the enzyme amylase.

They kept one of these tubes at room temperature and placed the other in a water bath at body temperature. They took samples from each tube every minute and mixed them with iodine on a spotting tile. Iodine turns blue-black in the presence of starch. The results are shown below.

Starch only at room temperature

Starch and amylase at room temperature

Starch and amylase at body temperature

a What effect does amylase have on starch? What is your evidence for this?
b What do the results tell you about the effect of temperature on the action of the enzyme amylase?
c Why is one tube of starch solution kept at room temperature without the addition of the enzyme?
d What do you predict would happen to the activity of the enzyme if acid from the stomach was added to the mixture?

1 Copy and complete the following sentences. Use the words below to fill the gaps.

gut   soluble   dissolve   digested   bloodstream

Once foods have been broken down to form small .... molecules, the process of digestion is complete.

Molecules of .... food are small enough to be absorbed through the .... wall. They are also soluble so they will .... into the .... which transports them to all parts of the body.

2 **a** What is peristalsis?

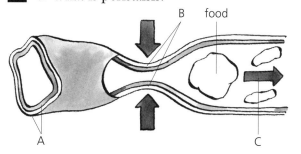

b Copy the diagram that shows food moving through the intestine. Use the labels below in place of the letters A–C on your diagram.
  • The direction the food is pushed in.
  • Layers of muscle in the wall of the intestine.
  • Muscles contract to squeeze food along.

3 Below is a diagram of villi in the small intestine.

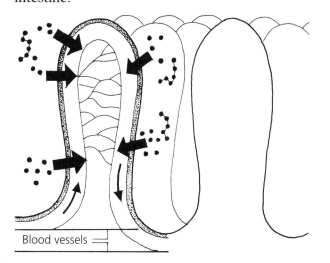

Blood vessels

Digested food is absorbed by the villi and passed into the blood to be transported around the body. How does the structure of the villi enable food to be absorbed effectively in the small intestine?

4 You can make a model gut using visking tubing. In an investigation students set up three model guts, each standing in a beaker of water.

In gut A they placed starch solution and in gut B they placed starch solution and the digestive enzyme amylase. Both of these were kept at room temperature.

In gut C they placed starch solution and amylase and kept it at body temperature. They tested the water surrounding the tubing at intervals for the presence of both starch and glucose.

The students used iodine solution to test for starch. Iodine solution is yellow when starch is not present and blue-black when starch is present.

They used Benedict's test for glucose. If the Benedict's solution remains blue this indicates there is no glucose present. If it turns orange/red this indicates the presence of glucose.

The table shows their results.

Iodine	Gut A	Gut B	Gut C
after 2 mins	yellow	yellow	yellow
after 5 mins	yellow	yellow	yellow
after 20 mins	yellow	yellow	yellow

Benedict's	Gut A	Gut B	Gut C
after 2 mins	blue	blue	orange
after 5 mins	blue	blue	orange
after 20 mins	blue	orange	orange

Explain the results for each of the model guts.

6 *The breath of life*

1 Copy and complete the following sentences. Use the words below to fill the gaps.

**breathing structures   breathing system
carbon dioxide   lungs   air passages**

The job of your .... is to get fresh supplies of air containing oxygen into your .... , and to get rid of waste .... produced by your body.

The breathing system has three main parts, the .... (which connect the lungs with the outside air), the alveoli and the .... (made of bone and muscle).

2 Look carefully at the words and definitions. Match each word to its definition and then copy them out.

Alveoli   the smallest air passages in the lungs.

Trachea   the upper part of the body containing the lungs.

Lungs   the main air passage leading in from the mouth and nose.

Diaphragm   the body organs where gas exchange takes place.

Bronchioles   millions of tiny air sacs making up the gas exchange tissue.

Thorax   large sheet of muscle separating the thorax from the abdomen.

3   **a** Copy and complete the following sentences. Choose the correct word from each of the pairs given.

Oxygen / Ozone and **glycogen / glucose** react together in your body to produce **excretion / energy**. This process is **respiration / breathing**. Carbon **dioxide / monoxide** and **waste / water** are produced as by-products of respiration.

b Use part **a** to help you complete the equation for respiration.

.... + ... $\longrightarrow$ .... +
....   + ...

4 For gas exchange in the lungs to work effectively we need to move air in and out of the lungs regularly. This we do by breathing. Our breathing movements involve the diaphragm and the muscles between the ribs. Explain carefully, using diagrams if you feel they will help, the events which take place

a when you breathe in
b when you breathe out.

5 The table shows the effect of exercise on the breathing rate of three people.

Activity	Number of breaths taken per minute...		
	Person A	Person B	Person C
Rest	21	15	18
20 step-ups per minute	29	21	25
50 step-ups per minute	40	30	34

a Plot a bar chart for these results to make it easier to compare them.
b Which person do you think is the fittest of the three, and which do you think is the least fit? Explain your answers.
c What else would happen to the breathing, as well as the rate going up?
d Why does our breathing change when we exercise?

1 Copy the diagram of a person. Use the labels below in place of the letters A–D on your diagram.

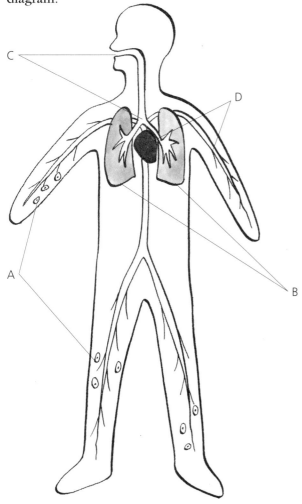

- You breathe to take air in and out of the body.
- In your lungs you exchange waste carbon dioxide from the blood for oxygen from the air.
- Your circulatory system makes sure every cell in the body gets the oxygen it needs.
- In the cells of your body, respiration takes place as you use the oxygen from the air to release the energy from your food. Carbon dioxide and water are produced as waste products.

2 The air you breathe in contains about 20% oxygen and only 0.04% carbon dioxide. The air you breathe out contains about 16% oxygen and 4% carbon dioxide. What happens in your lungs to bring about this change?

3

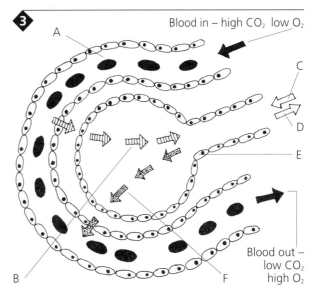

Blood in – high CO_2 low O_2

Blood out – low CO_2 high O_2

The alveoli are specialised structures that allow the exchange of gases in the lungs. The diagram shows a single alveolus.

a Copy and label this diagram.

b Describe *three* features of alveoli which make the exchange of gases as effective as possible.

4 Explain why the diseases below lead to a lack of oxygen in the body.

a In cystic fibrosis the lung cells produce a very thick, sticky mucus which fills the alveoli and blocks the bronchioles. It makes lung infections more likely and the lungs have to be cleared of mucus by physiotherapy at least twice a day.

People with cystic fibrosis are often short of breath, particularly just before they have physiotherapy.

b Emphysema is a disease often caused by smoking. The structure of the alveoli breaks down, resulting in lungs with much larger air sacs than normal. These large spaces may fill with fluid.

People with emphysema are always short of breath and as the disease gets worse they may need to breathe pure oxygen.

c In asthma the linings of the air passages swell and produce extra mucus. During an asthma attack people find it very hard to breathe and the air is forced in and out of their chests with a wheezing sound.

8 *Blood – supplying your needs*

1 Copy and complete the following sentences. Use the words below to fill the gaps.

circulatory   transported   heart   glucose blood   waste products   oxygen

Substances are .... round the body in the .... Food molecules such as .... and substances such as .... are carried to the cells where they are needed.

The blood also collects and carries away .... from the cells. The .... system is made up of the blood, the blood vessels and the ....

2 Copy and complete this table, using the words and sentences from the list below.

Part of the blood	Description
a	The liquid part of the blood. Pale yellow and made mainly of water, it contains dissolved food molecules and other chemicals.
red blood cells	**b**
white blood cells	**c**
d	These are small fragments of cells with no nucleus. They help to clot the blood.

- Platelets.
- These cells have a nucleus and help to defend the body against microbes which cause disease.
- Plasma.
- These cells have no nucleus. They are packed with the red pigment haemoglobin which carries oxygen.

3 The plasma is very important for transporting substances round the body. Three of the main substances are carbon dioxide, urea and digested food.

a For each substance say where in the body it enters the plasma.

b For each substance say where it is transported to, and what happens to it when it gets there.

4 The red blood cells can carry oxygen around the body because they are packed with a red pigment called haemoglobin which picks up oxygen to form oxyhaemoglobin. This carries oxygen to places which need it and gives it up, forming haemoglobin and oxygen.

Copy the diagram to show where in the body oxygen is picked up by the red blood cells and where it is unloaded. Use the labels below on your diagram.
- oxygen in
- oxygen out
- red cells containing oxyhaemoglobin
- red cells containing haemoglobin (without oxygen)

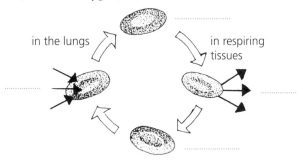

in the lungs

in respiring tissues

5 The number of red blood cells in 1 mm³ of normal human blood is around 5000 million. However, there are certain situations where the numbers of red blood cells in the blood may be particularly high or low. For each of the examples below, explain the effect the difference in the red blood cell count will have on the person.

a A person living at high altitude (where the air contains less oxygen) will have a higher red blood cell count than someone living at low altitude.

b An athlete who has used the illegal practice of 'blood doping' will have a higher than normal red blood cell count. Blood doping involves taking blood from themselves and storing it for several weeks, and then having a blood transfusion of their own blood the day before a competition.

c A person who does not have sufficient iron in their diet will be anaemic, feeling very tired and lacking in energy. Their red blood count will be lower than normal.

1 Copy and complete the following sentences. Use the words below to fill the gaps.

circulatory system **pumps** **blood vessels** **capillaries** **heart**

Blood flows around your body through a network of .... that make up the .... Your blood is kept flowing round this system by the action of the ....

The heart is a muscular bag which .... the blood through the system. The blood vessels are the arteries, veins and ....

2 Copy and complete the following sentences, choosing the correct ending in each case.

a Blood enters.....
b The atria contract and.....
c The ventricles contract and.....
d The blood leaving the right-hand side of the heart.....
e The blood leaving the left-hand side of the heart.....

Choose the endings from:
• ....force blood out of the heart.
• ....is pumped to the lungs.
• ....is pumped around the body.
• ....force blood into the ventricles.
• ....the atria of the heart.

3 The diagram shows the double circulation of the human heart. Use it to help you answer the following questions.

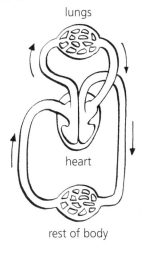

lungs

heart

rest of body

a Copy the diagram (at the bottom of the previous column) and shade it blue in the areas where the blood is deoxygenated and red in the areas where you would expect oxygenated blood.
b What happens to the blood in the body?
c What happens to the blood in the lungs?
d Why is it called a double circulation?

4 There are three main types of blood vessels in the human body.

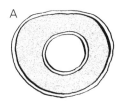 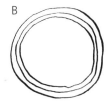

A   B   C

a Name the three types of blood vessel A, B and C.
b Describe the job of each type of blood vessel in the body.

5 Here are descriptions of two heart problems and how they may be overcome. In each case use what you know about the heart and the circulatory system to explain the problems caused by the condition and how the treatment helps.

a Sometimes babies are born with a 'hole in the heart' – there is a gap in the central dividing wall of the heart. The babies may look blue in colour and will have very little energy.

Surgeons can close up the hole.

b The blood vessels supplying blood to the heart muscle itself may become clogged with fatty material. The person affected may get chest pain when they exercise or even have a heart attack.

Doctors may be able to replace the clogged up blood vessels with bits of healthy blood vessels taken from other parts of the patient's body.

10 Releasing energy

1 Copy and complete the following sentences. Use the words below to fill the gaps.

heat   energy   food   fuels   glucose

When .... like coal burn they release their stored energy as .... Living organisms take in their fuel as .... The main fuel which provides your body with the .... it needs is ....

2 Copy and complete the following sentences, choosing the correct ending in each case.

a Energy is released from glucose.....
b During respiration chemical reactions take place.....
c When glucose reacts with oxygen.....
d Carbon dioxide and water.....
e Because it uses oxygen from the air the process.....

Choose the endings from:
* .....energy is released.
* .....is known as aerobic respiration.
* .....are formed as waste products.
* .....by a process called respiration.
* .....inside the cells of your body.

3 It is very important for your body to have a regular supply of food to provide energy for your cells.

If you don't get enough to eat you become thin and stop growing. You will become weak and tired, not wanting to move around and you will start to feel very cold.

What are the three *main* uses of the energy released in your body during respiration?

4 When you move around normally you produce the energy your body needs by aerobic respiration. If you are exercising hard and there is not enough oxygen reaching your muscles your body gets its energy using anaerobic respiration.

a Give a word equation for aerobic respiration.
b What does anaerobic respiration produce?
c What is the main advantage of anaerobic respiration?
d What is the main disadvantage of anaerobic respiration?

5 The diagram shows the breathing rate of a young person taking part in a 400 m race on Sports Day.

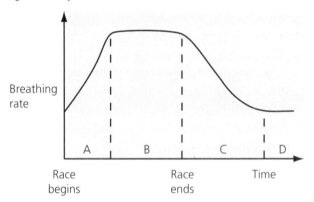

Use your knowledge of breathing and respiration to explain the four areas shown on the graph.

11 Making the body work hard

1 Read this passage and use it to answer the questions. Answer in complete sentences.

Everything you do needs energy – moving, keeping warm, growing and even sleeping. The energy comes from the food you eat.

Some foods, like pasta and bread, contain lots of energy which your body can release steadily. Other foods, like celery, contain very little energy. The energy is released from your food in the process of respiration.

If you take in more energy than you need for your way of life, your body will store the extra as fat.

But if you don't take in enough energy your health will suffer – you lose weight, start using your own body tissues for energy and you may even die.

a Give three examples of how your body uses energy.

b What sort of food would you eat before running a marathon race and why?

c How does your body release the energy from your food?

d What happens if you take in more energy than you need?

e Why is it so serious if you don't take in enough energy over a long time?

2 Our bodies need energy all the time to stay alive and work properly. Explain why we need energy

a when we are asleep

b for growing even when we are grown up.

3 The diagram shows the way the blood flow to different parts of your body changes when you exercise hard. Explain why each of the changes **a-d** takes place.

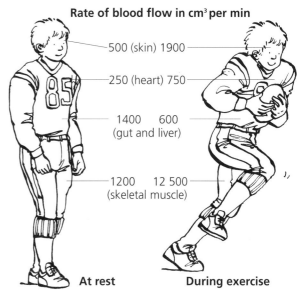

Rate of blood flow in cm³ per min

500 (skin) 1900

250 (heart) 750

1400 600 (gut and liver)

1200 12 500 (skeletal muscle)

At rest   **During exercise**

a The blood supply to the skin increases.

b The blood supply to the heart increases.

c The blood supply to the gut is decreased.

d The muscles get a much bigger flow of blood.

4 Use the table at the bottom of the page to answer the questions.

a Work out the volume of air (cm³) taken into the lungs over one minute
i at rest   **ii** after 5 minutes gentle exercise
iii after 10 minutes hard exercise.

b Use your results from part **a** to draw a bar chart showing the effect of exercise on the lungs.

c Why is it important that the amount of air taken into your body changes as you exercise?

d Explain briefly what happens to the blood flow through the heart during periods of exercise.

Table for Q4	Number of breaths per minute	Volume of each breath (cm³)	Pulse beats per minute	Volume of blood pumped per beat (cm³)
At rest	18	450	72	65
After 5 minutes gentle exercise	25	600	80	85
After 10 minutes hard exercise	41	1050	90	120

12 *Fit for life*

1 Copy and complete the following sentences. Use the words below to fill the gaps.

exercise   circulation   heart   fit   healthy

Being .... is important – it helps to keep our bodies .... and lets us carry out all the everyday activities in our life.

Regular .... improves your fitness. It has an effect on your muscles, ..., breathing and ....

2 Here are five sentences describing some of the effects of fitness on your body. Only three of them are scientifically correct. Choose and copy the correct sentences.

A Your risk of a heart attack or a stroke decreases because of your improved circulation.

B Your breathing becomes shallower and you take in less air with each breath.

C Your muscles become larger and are able to work longer and harder.

D The risk of a heart attack or a stroke increases because of the stress placed on your body.

E As your heart muscle becomes stronger your blood is pumped around your body more efficiently.

3 It is often said that taking regular exercise and getting fit is good for your heart and lungs.

a Draw bar charts to show the data given in the table.

	Before getting fit	After getting fit
Amount of blood pumped out of the heart during each beat (cm³)	64	80
Heart volume (cm³)	120	140
Breathing rate (no. of breaths per minute)	14	12
Pulse rate	72	63

b Use the information on the bar charts from part **a** to explain exactly what effect increased fitness has on
i your heart   **ii** your lungs.

4 **a** It is said that measuring the pulse rate before and after exercise is a good way to assess the fitness of an individual. Why is this?

Three 20-year-old students took part in an experiment to measure their fitness. Their resting pulse was measured and recorded. They then exercised hard for 4 minutes, followed by a recovery period. Their pulse rate was recorded at intervals. The information is shown in the table.

Time (minutes)	Pulse rate per minute...		
	Student A	Student B	Student C
0 (resting pulse)	75	80	65
1 (exercise)	95	100	85
2 (exercise)	115	120	105
3 (exercise)	135	140	125
4 (exercise)	160	170	150
6 (recovery)	135	150	120
9 (recovery)	105	125	80
15 (recovery)	90	105	65

b Plot a graph to show the pulse rates of students A, B and C during the experiment.

c Which student was the fittest?

d Which student was the least fit?

e How does the data on the graph show the different fitness levels of the students?

13 Microscopic killers

1 Copy and complete the following sentences. Use the words below to fill the gaps.

unhygienic   microbes   bacteria   disease toxins   infected

Many diseases are caused when microbes such as certain .... and viruses get into the body.

A person is more likely to develop a .... if large numbers of .... enter their body. This can happen by being in .... conditions or by being in contact with someone who is already .... with the disease.

Once bacteria and viruses are in the body they reproduce rapidly and may release poisons called .... which make you feel ill.

2 Bacteria and viruses are very small. Bacteria have a structure a bit like a plant cell with cytoplasm inside a cell wall, but their genetic material is not contained within a nucleus.

Viruses are smaller than bacteria and they are made up of a simple protein coat containing a small amount of genetic material.

Copy the diagrams of a bacterium and a virus. Use the information above to label the diagrams.

Bacterium

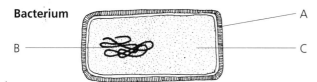

Virus

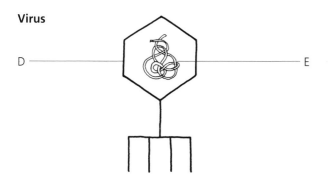

3 Some bacteria cause diseases but many others are useful to us, for example making cheese and yoghurt, rotting down dead tissue and keeping our guts healthy. However, *all* viruses cause disease in the living organisms they infect.

Copy the diagrams of viruses reproducing. Label the diagrams and use them to explain how viruses cause disease.

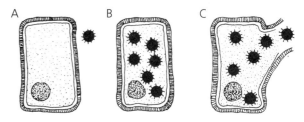

4 Flu is a viral disease which affects the lining of your breathing passages. You catch it by breathing in viruses coughed or breathed out by someone who already has the disease.

With flu you get a high temperature, sore throat, aching muscles and joints and a headache, and feel very unwell until your body fights off the infection.

Cholera, on the other hand, is bacterial, and is spread through dirty water in areas of poor sanitation.

The main symptom of cholera is severe diarrhoea. It can be cured with antibiotics but most people recover by themselves if they are able to keep drinking clean water. The best approach is to prevent the disease happening in the first place.

Copy and complete this table showing some facts about flu and cholera.

Disease	Influenza (flu)	Cholera	Other illness
Caused by	virus	**D**	
Spread by	**A**	**E**	
Symptoms	**B**	severe diarrhoea	
How can it be prevented or cured?	**C**	**F**	

Fill in the empty column with details of some other illness you may have had yourself, e.g. a cold, chickenpox, tonsillitis, etc.

5 Design a leaflet to be used around your school to show other pupils how to avoid the spread of diseases caused by microbes.

1 Copy and complete the following sentences. Use the words below to fill the gaps.

defences   microbes   white blood cells

We live in a world full of disease-causing .... We can try to avoid them, but when we do come into contact with them we need

....

Our skin prevents many microbes from entering our bodies, and if they do get in our .... will destroy them, although we may feel ill first.

2 Look carefully at the words and definitions below. Match each word to its definition and then copy them out.

Skin a sticky liquid which traps microbes in the breathing system.

Blood clots acts as a barrier preventing microbes getting into the body.

Mucus tiny hair-like projections which move mucus and trapped microbes from the breathing system to the throat for swallowing.

Cilia form to seal cuts, preventing microbes getting in and too much blood getting out.

3 If disease-causing bacteria or viruses get inside your body, then your immune system starts working.

Some white blood cells make antibodies which destroy microbes. The diagrams show another way in which white blood cells help to defend you against disease.

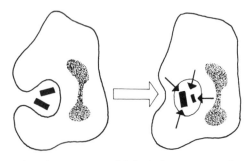

Copy the diagrams and label them to explain what is happening.

4 **a** Once you have had a disease, you are unlikely to get it again because you will have developed natural immunity. How does this work?

b In some cases you are vaccinated against a disease (e.g. polio, tetanus) which gives you artificial immunity. How does this work?

5 Read this case history and use it together with the diagram to answer the questions that follow.

Tuberculosis (TB) is one of the most common infectious diseases in the world. There are an estimated 20 million people with TB and about 3.3 million people die each year.

TB is very infectious and is spread by droplets of moisture coughed out by a TB sufferer. Crowded conditions at home and work allow TB to spread rapidly. If these conditions improve, there are fewer cases.

TB can be treated by a long course of antibiotics, or it can be prevented by vaccinating children before they have the disease.

TB used to be very common in the UK, but it is now rare. The diagram shows the numbers of cases in the UK between 1913 and 1990.

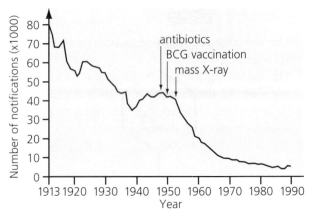

a What has been the trend in the number of cases of TB since 1950?

b How would you explain this trend?

c Do you think this data justifies the introduction of a worldwide vaccination programme against TB? Explain your reasoning.

1 Copy and complete the following sentences. Use the words below to fill the gaps.

sensitivity slow movement reproduce excrete

All plants and animals do seven things: they .... , respire, grow, ... , react to their environment and use food for energy.

Some of these are easier to observe than others, and .... is one of the clearest. This is usually fairly fast in animals, and although it is usually in .... plants it can still be observed.

Most living organisms move towards things that they need and away from things that are harmful, showing .... by responding to change.

2 Animals and plants are sensitive to their environment and respond to any changes (stimuli) in it. The following sentences describe various responses to stimuli. For each one say what the stimulus is and which sense organ responds to it.

E.g. Spot the dog heard his master call him and so he ran away across the field.

The stimulus was the sound of the call which was detected by Spot's ears.

a The sailors were relieved to see the flash of light from the lighthouse.
b The flickering tongue of the snake picked up the scent of the rabbit in the air.
c He screamed and dropped the hot pan as soon as he picked it up.
d The small child smiled as she sucked on the ice lolly.

3 Copy and complete this table which shows some of the organs in the human body and what they do.

Organ	What it does
heart	**a**
stomach	**b**
c	co-ordinates all the messages from the sense organs and sends out messages to the body
eye	**d**

4

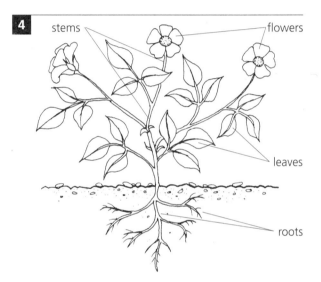

Like many animals, plants have organs to carry out particular jobs. What are the main jobs of

a the leaves
b the stem
c the roots
d the flowers.

5 All living organisms need energy for the maintenance of life.

a What do we call the process by which animals and plants release energy from their food?
b How do green plants obtain the energy they need for life?
c All animals depend on plants for their survival. Explain how this happens.

1 Match each plant organ to its description, and then copy them out.

Leaves   anchor the plant firmly in the ground.

Stems   allow sexual reproduction to take place.

Roots   use energy from light to make food.

Flowers hold the plant upright and transport substances between the various parts.

2 Copy this diagram of a typical green plant cell, and add the correct description from the list below to each label.

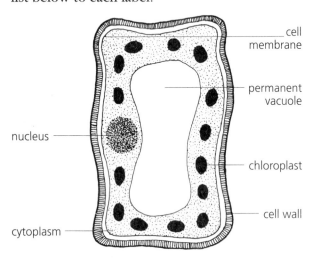

cell membrane

permanent vacuole

nucleus

chloroplast

cell wall

cytoplasm

A Controls all the activities of the cell.
B The 'jelly' in which most of the chemical reactions take place.
C Controls the movement of substances in and out of the cell.
D Filled with cell sap it acts as part of the 'skeleton' of the plant.
E Made of cellulose, it strengthens the cell and also acts as part of the 'skeleton' of the plant.
F Absorbs energy from light to make food.

3 Leaves are the plant organs which make food. They use light energy which is absorbed by chloroplasts.

Palisade cells contain lots of chloroplasts and in a leaf they are packed tightly together near to the top to absorb as much light as possible. This is called the palisade layer.

The surface of the leaf is covered by epidermal cells which are transparent so that light can reach the palisade tissue beneath. The epidermis protects the leaf from water loss and damage. The upper epidermis is on the top surface. The lower epidermis is on the under surface and it has holes in it called stomata. The stomata can be opened and closed to let gases in and out.

Between the lower epidermis and the palisade tissue is the spongy layer. The cells here are packed very loosely. They have a large surface area and big air spaces, making it easier for gases to move in and out of the cells.

Use this information to help you answer the questions below.

a Copy this diagram of the leaf and add the labels below.

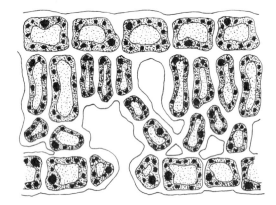

A Paliside layer.   **D** Upper epidermis.
B Spongy layer.   **E** Chloroplasts.
C Lower epidermis.   **F** Stoma.

b Give the functions of the parts of a leaf you have labelled.

4 Plants make food in one organ and take up water from the soil in another organ. But both food and water are needed all over the plant.

a Where do plants take in water?
b There are two transport tissues in a plant. One is the phloem. What is the other?
c Which transport tissue carries food?
d Which transport tissue carries water?
e What is the main difference between the cells of the two transport systems?

3 The energy factory

1 Copy and complete the following sentences. Use the words below to fill the gaps.

water   chloroplasts   starch photosynthesis   light   chlorophyll sugar (glucose)

Plants produce their own food in a process known as ....

They absorb .... energy using a green chemical called .... which is found in .... in the plant cells.

Carbon dioxide and .... are joined together using this energy to form .... and oxygen.

The glucose produced in photosynthesis may be converted into insoluble .... for storage.

2 **a** Match each word related to photosynthesis to its description and then copy them out.

Carbon dioxide gas	is produced and released into the air.
Water	provides energy.
Sunlight	from the root moves up to the leaf through the stem.
Sugars	is absorbed from the air.
Oxygen	are made in the leaf and provide the plant with food.

b Write a word equation for photosynthesis.

3 Copy the diagram of a leaf. Use the labels at the top of the next column on your diagram.

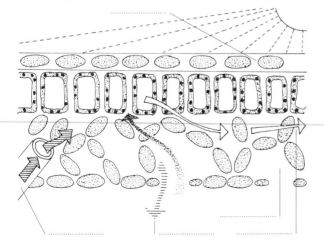

A Oxygen moves out.
B The epidermis is a clear protective layer which lets sunlight in.
C Sugars dissolve and are taken to other parts of the plant.
D Stomata (pores) let gases in and out.
E Water is brought from the roots in xylem vessels.

4 **a** Much of the glucose made in photosynthesis is turned into an insoluble storage compound. What is this compound?

b Some plants, like potatoes, develop special storage organs where they keep stored food to help them survive the winter. One potato farmer recorded the amount of sunlight each month that her potato crop was growing. She also recorded the average crop of potatoes she got from her plants when she harvested them. Explain her findings.

Amount of sunlight each month of the growing season	Mass of potato crop per plant
average	1 kg
poor	0.5 kg
high	1.5 kg

5 The glucose produced during photosynthesis is used for a number of things in the cells of the plant.

a Copy and complete this table about three substances which may be made from the glucose.

Substance made	Role/roles in the plant
i	storage compound
cellulose	ii
protein	iii

b The glucose made by photosynthesis is not only used to make other chemicals. What is the other main use of the glucose produced in the leaves?

4 Bigger and better crops

1 Copy and complete the following sentences. Use the words below to fill the gaps.

temperature   carbon dioxide   light limit   oxygen   photosynthesis

During .... a plant uses the energy from sunlight to turn .... and water into glucose and .... This needs a plentiful supply of carbon dioxide and ....

The .... is also important – it must not be too hot or too cold. If any of these is not right it will .... the amount of photosynthesis which takes place.

2 Here is the apparatus you would need to demonstrate photosynthesis taking place in *Elodea* (pond weed).

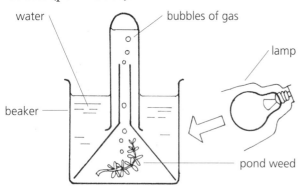

a How do you know when photosynthesis is actually taking place?

The rate of photosynthesis is measured by recording the rate at which bubbles are produced.

b What would you expect to happen to the rate at which bubbles are produced if you moved
 i the light closer to the pondweed
 ii the light further away from the pondweed?
c Why would you expect moving the light to affect the rate of photosynthesis?
d Which other factor might be changing each time you move the lamp?

3 The figures in the table (at the top of the next column) show the mean growth of two sets of oak seedlings. One set was grown in 85% of full sunlight, the other set in only 35% of full sunlight.

| Year | Mean height of seedlings (cm)... | |
	85% full sunlight	35% full sunlight
1966	12	10
1967	16	12.5
1968	18	14
1969	21	17
1970	28	20
1971	35	21
1972	36	23

a Plot a graph to show the growth of both sets of oak seedlings.
b Explain the difference in the growth of the two sets of seedlings using what you know about photosynthesis and limiting factors.

4 The graph shows the effect of temperature on photosynthesis and respiration for a tomato plant.

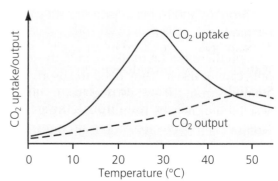

a At what temperature is photosynthesis in the tomato plant at a maximum?
b What effect does temperature have on the rate of photosynthesis in the tomato plant?
c At what temperature is respiration in the tomato plant at a maximum?
d To get the maximum yield of tomatoes, the plants need to be grown at their optimal temperature. This is the point at which the rate of photosynthesis exceeds the rate of respiration by the largest amount. Why will this result in the biggest crop of tomatoes?
e What temperature will give the maximum yield from tomato plants?

1   Copy and complete the following sentences. Use the words below to fill the gaps.

propagator cuttings light transpiration humid

When gardeners take cuttings they often put them in a special .... or even in a polythene bag. This gives the cuttings a warm, ... atmosphere. If they are also given plenty of .... they have ideal conditions for successful growth.

It is important for .... to be in a humid atmosphere so they do not lose too much water by ....

2   Read this passage and use it to help you answer the questions which follow. Answer in complete sentences.

Plants can make their own sugars by photosynthesis, but for healthy growth they need proteins and to make proteins they must have nitrogen.

Although there is a lot of nitrogen in the air, plants cannot use it. They need to absorb (take in) nitrates from the soil through their roots. These nitrates may be from the decaying bodies of animals and plants, or they may come from fertilisers added to the soil.

a Why do plants need nitrates?
b How do plants take in nitrates?
c What are the possible sources of the nitrates in the soil?
d If nitrates from fertilisers put on the soil find their way into rivers, they often lead to the rapid growth of algae and eventually the death of all living things in the river. Why does this happen?

The diagram (at the bottom of the previous column) is of the apparatus which can show how much water a plant loses by transpiration. Use the diagram to help you answer these questions.

a What is transpiration?
b What part of the leaves helps to prevent them from losing too much water under normal conditions?
c If the top surfaces of the leaves were coated with Vaseline, how do you think it would affect the rate at which the plant takes up and loses water?
d If the bottom surfaces of the leaves were coated in Vaseline, how do you think it would affect the rate at which the plant takes up and loses water?
e What do you think would happen to the air bubble in the capillary tube if you turned a fan onto the leaves of the plant? Explain your answer.
f What is the apparatus actually measuring?

4   Plants need certain nutrients to grow well.

Nutrients	Part played in the plant
nitrates (N)	• leaf and shoot production • producing proteins (building blocks and enzymes)
phosphates (P)	• helps in the reactions of photosynthesis and respiration
potassium (K)	• good for flowers, fruit and disease resistance

At a plant clinic run by a fertiliser manufacturer, a number of farmers turn up with plants which are not growing as well as they should. For each plant, explain what is wrong with it and suggest what needs to be done to the soil to make sure that the crop improves and grows well.

Plant A has yellow leaves with dead brown spots. Crops grown in the field the previous year produced poor flowers and little fruit.

Plant B shows stunted growth, and the older leaves have turned pale and yellow.

Plant C has poor growth of both stems and roots. The young leaves show a purple colour.

3

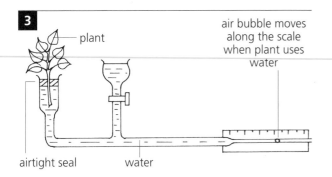

plant

air bubble moves along the scale when plant uses water

airtight seal   water

6 Watering holes

1 Copy and complete the following sentences. Use the words below to fill the gaps.

waxy   support   stomata   transpiration

Water inside plant cells provides the plant with .... Plants lose water vapour by evaporation through the .... (pores) in their leaves. This is known as ....

Most plants have a .... waterproof layer on their leaves which stops them losing too much water.

2 Copy the diagrams of a leaf. Use the labels below on your diagrams.

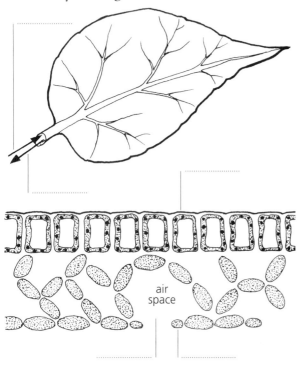

A Xylem tissue in the veins brings water to the leaves.

B Guard cells open and close the stomata, giving some control over water loss.

C The waxy cuticle on the top surface of the leaf helps prevent unwanted water loss.

D Phloem tissue in the veins takes sugars away from the leaf to all parts of the plant.

E Stomata in the lower surface of the leaf allow carbon dioxide to diffuse into the leaf and water vapour to be lost by evaporation.

3 Copy and complete the following sentences, choosing the correct ending in each case.

a Water loss by evaporation in a plant.....
b Transpiration is more rapid in.....
c Plants keep relatively cool in hot sun.....
d Transpiration also creates a risk.....

Choose the endings from:
- .....hot, dry and windy conditions.
- .....that the plant will lose too much water and wilt.
- .....because transpiration cools them down.
- .....is known as transpiration.

4 The diagram shows an experiment which is a model of osmosis in living cells.

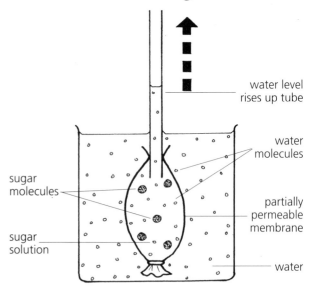

a Explain what is happening in the experiment.
b How is this model useful in explaining the entry of water into the xylem from the soil?
c Using your knowledge of osmosis and diffusion, explain why plants store all their excess carbohydrate as insoluble starch.
d Osmosis and diffusion take place along concentration gradients. When mineral ions such as nitrates are taken into plant roots they are often moved against a concentration gradient. What is this movement called?
e How does transpiration help in moving water up through the plant?
f Why is it an advantage for the roots to have a large surface area?

7 Plant growth responses

1 Copy and complete the following sentences. Use the words below to fill the gaps.

hormones   growing   stimuli   light gravity

Plants usually respond slowly to changes in their surroundings (called ....). They are sensitive to .... , moisture and the force of ....

Plants respond by .... towards or away from a stimulus. The response is coordinated and controlled by .... produced by the plant.

2 Plant shoots and roots respond differently to stimuli. Copy and complete the following sentences. Choose the correct word from each of the pairs given.

a Plant shoots grow **towards / away from** light.
b Plant shoots grow **against / with** gravity.
c Plant roots grow **towards / away from** moisture.
d Plant roots grow **against / with** gravity.

3 The diagrams show shoot tips treated in different ways and then exposed to light from one direction only.

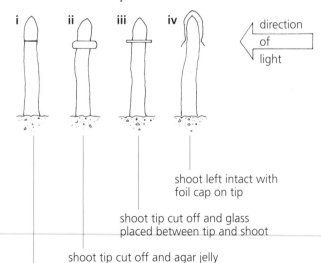

i
ii
iii
iv

direction of light

shoot left intact with foil cap on tip

shoot tip cut off and glass placed between tip and shoot

shoot tip cut off and agar jelly placed between tip and shoot

shoot tip cut off and replaced

a Copy the diagrams from the bottom of the previous column. Under each part draw how you would expect the shoot tip to look after two days.
b Explain what has happened in each case.

The diagram below shows a shoot tip which has bent over in response to light from one direction only.

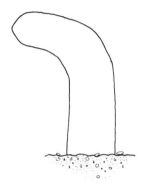

c Copy the diagram. Add arrows and labels to show
   i the direction the light is coming from
   ii which side of the shoot has more of the hormone auxin.

4 Since we have found out about plant hormones we have developed a number of ways of using them to affect and control the ways plants behave. Explain carefully how we use plant hormones

a to produce large numbers of new plants quickly
b to regulate the ripening of fruit
c to kill weeds.

5 The figures in the table show the increases in UK crop yields between 1885 and 1984.

Crop	Yield (in tonnes per hectare)...		
	1885–89	1950–54	1984
wheat	2.06	2.81	7.71
barley	1.96	2.62	5.59
potatoes	14.70	19.90	37.00

Write a brief article for a country magazine (using bar charts if you want to) explaining as well as you can *all* of the different factors which might have led to these increases in yields.

8 Responding to change

1 We have sense organs containing special receptors which allow us to detect changes both in the world around us and inside our own bodies. Using this information we can react to our surroundings. Copy and complete this table, which shows some of our most important sense organs, using the words and phrases from the list below.

Position of the receptors	What are the receptor cells sensitive to?
eyes	a
ears	b
c	changes in position – important for keeping our balance
tongue	d
e	chemicals – enable us to smell
skin	f

- Light
- Pressure and temperature changes
- Inner ear
- Sound
- Nose
- Chemicals - enable us to taste

2 Copy and complete the following sentences. Use the words below to fill the gaps.

responds stimulus coordinates senses nervous receptors

Your .... system enables your body to detect and respond quickly to stimuli. A .... is a change in your surroundings or a change inside your body. Your .... make you aware of these changes using special .... which detect different kinds of stimuli. The rest of your nervous system .... all the information and controls the way your body ....

3 The nervous system is made up of a number of parts. Explain the job of each of these parts.

a The sense organs.
b The central nervous system.
c The sensory nerves.
d The motor nerves.

4 a What is the main difference between a voluntary action and a reflex action?
b What is the value of reflex actions to the body?
c Analyse the following reflex actions using the sequence

stimulus ⟶ receptor ⟶ coordinator ⟶ effector ⟶ response

   i a doctor hits you just below the knee cap with a rubber hammer
   ii you put your bare foot down on a drawing pin
   iii someone claps their hands near your face.

5 The diagram shows the receptors, nerves and muscles involved in a reflex action.

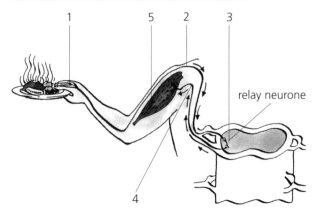

relay neurone

a Write a description of what is happening at each of the numbered points 1–5.
b How do you know consciously what has happened in a reflex action like this?

9 The way of seeing

1 The diagram shows the eye, with various parts labelled.

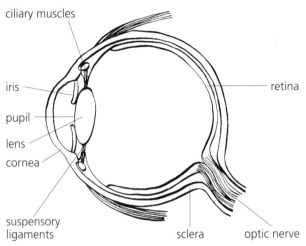

ciliary muscles

iris

pupil

lens

cornea

suspensory ligaments

retina

sclera

optic nerve

Copy and complete this table, matching the parts of the eye to the correct description of their functions.

Part of the eye	Function
a	contains receptor cells which are sensitive to light
b	tough white outer layer
c	muscle which changes the size of the pupil
d	curved, transparent area at the front of the eye
e	focuses the image on the retina
f	sensory neurones carry impulses from the retina to the brain
g	hole that allows light into the eye
h	change the shape of the lens
i	attach the ciliary muscles to the lens

2 The pupil of the eye is the hole through which light enters. The size of the pupil is controlled by the muscles of the iris and the pupil changes size depending on the light levels.

Draw diagrams to show what the pupil and iris of an eye would look like
a in very bright light
b in ordinary light levels
c in very dim light.

3 Here is some information about three eye problems. Explain why these conditions affect sight.

a With cataracts the cornea goes cloudy or milky.
b Some people have an eyeball which is more egg shaped than round. They are often short sighted – they can focus objects close to them but not those at a distance.
c If the retina of the eye becomes detached, people go completely blind in that eye.

4 Copy the diagrams below and add to them to help you answer the following questions.

a How do we focus on objects which are near to us?

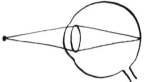

b How do we focus on distant objects?

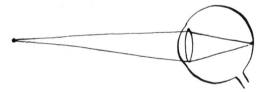

c Show how the image which is formed on the retina is actually upside down.

d A scientist asked people to wear a special headset which seemed to turn everything upside down. For several days they saw an upside down world. Eventually they started seeing things the right way up again. When they stopped wearing the headset everything appeared upside down! After a day or two their perception of the world returned to normal.

Can you work out what was happening at each stage of this experiment?

1 Copy and complete the following sentences. Use the words below to fill the gaps.

temperature sugar automatic control

In order to survive, our bodies need to keep themselves at just the right _____ , have just the right amount of water and _____ in the bloodstream and get rid of any poisonous waste products. Your body has _____ systems which constantly monitor and _____ these things.

2 Match each word to its definition and then copy them out.

Hormone a condition when the pancreas cannot make enough insulin to control the blood sugar .

Insulin a chemical message carried in the blood which causes a change in the body.

Diabetes a hormone made in the pancreas which causes sugar to pass from the blood into cells where it is needed for energy.

3 Some people develop diabetes in a relatively mild form. Their pancreas still makes insulin, but not enough to cope with the amount of carbohydrate and sugar-rich food they eat. This type of diabetes can be managed without needing to inject insulin. Explain how this might be done.

4 **a** Look at **graph A** below. Why does the level of insulin increase after a meal?
b **Graph B** below shows the blood sugar pattern of someone who has just developed diabetes and is not yet using injected insulin. What differences are there between this pattern and the one shown in **graph A**?
c **Graph C** below shows the effect of regular insulin injections on the blood sugar level of someone with diabetes. Why are the insulin injections so important to their health?

5 Control of the blood sugar level in the body is monitored and controlled by the hormones insulin and glucagon in the pancreas. Draw and label a diagram which shows clearly how this control is maintained.

Graphs for **Q4**

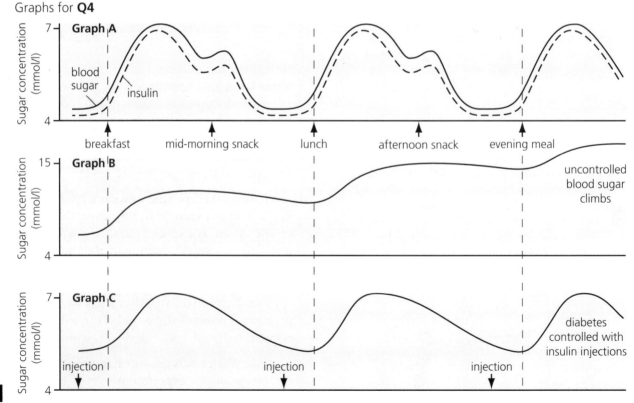

11 *Cleaning the bloodstream*

1 Copy and complete the following sentences. Use the words below to fill the gaps.

kidneys lungs amino acids urine waste respiration urea

The chemical reactions which take place in your body to keep you alive produce .... products which would be poisonous to your body if they were not removed.

Carbon dioxide produced by .... is removed through the .... when we breathe out.

When your liver breaks down excess .... (from proteins) .... is formed. This is removed from the blood by the .... and excreted as .... from the bladder.

2 If we take in a lot of liquid, the excess water is removed by our kidneys and we produce a lot of urine. Similarly, if we take in a heavy load of mineral ions, e.g. salt, our kidneys get rid of the excess. But our kidneys are not the only way we can control our water and salt loss.

a What are the two ways that water is lost from our bodies, other than in urine?
b What is the other way that excess salts are lost from our bodies, apart from in urine?
c How much glucose and protein would you expect to find in urine?

3 The blood flowing into a kidney tubule contains, amongst other things, glucose, dissolved ions, urea and some traces of alcohol.

Copy the diagram and make a table to explain what has happened to each of these substances at points A, B, C and D of the tubule.

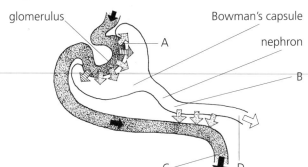

glomerulus   Bowman's capsule
          A   nephron
               B
    C   D

4 As part of an experiment a student drank a given volume of water. His urine output was then measured at 30 minute intervals for 150 minutes. The salt concentration of each urine sample was also measured. The bar charts show what happened to the volume of urine produced and the concentration of salt in the urine.

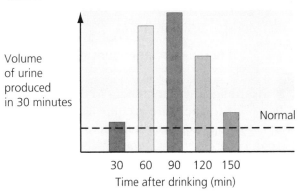

Volume of urine produced in 30 minutes

Normal

30 60 90 120 150
Time after drinking (min)

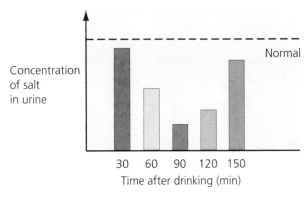

Concentration of salt in urine

Normal

30 60 90 120 150
Time after drinking (min)

a Describe what happened to the volume of urine produced by the student over the 150 minutes of the experiment.
b Explain how the hormone ADH is involved in the changes in the volume of urine produced.
c Describe what happened to the salt concentration of the urine over the same period.
d Why do these changes in salt concentration happen?
e What changes would you expect to see in the volume and salt concentration of urine if the student did not drink for 12 hours?

12 Keeping warm and staying cool

1 Copy and complete the following sentences. Use the words below to fill the gaps.

constant   sweating   enzymes   die

It is very important to maintain a .... body temperature of about 37 °C. This is the temperature at which all the .... in your body work at their best.

If your body temperature gets too high or too low you will .... We cool down by .... if our body temperature starts to go up.

2 Rearrange these sentences to describe how Sally's body temperature is controlled when it starts to go up. Copy the sentences out in the correct order.

- Her body temperature starts to rise.
- Sally takes a long, cool drink after she stops exercising to replace the liquid she has lost through sweating.
- Her temperature returns to normal.
- Her skin goes red and she starts to sweat; this increases the amount of heat lost through her skin.
- Sally exercises hard.

3 Here is some information about hypothermia. Use it to help you design a poster to help people avoid this problem, which is responsible for thousands of deaths in the UK every year.

- Hypothermia is when the body temperature drops below 35 °C and the normal working of the body is affected.
- Old people, small children and people exposed in bad weather conditions are most at risk.
- Up to 20% of your body heat is lost through your head.
- Warm clothing, adequate heating, regular meals, warm drinks and exercise all help to prevent hypothermia.
- People with hypothermia have greyish-blue, puffy faces and blue lips. Their skin feels very cold to the touch, and they will be drowsy with slurred speech. If the body temperature falls too low the sufferer will become unconscious and may die.

4 Explain the role of the following in maintaining a constant core body temperature

a the thermoregulatory centre in the brain
b the temperature sensors in the skin.

5 We humans maintain our body temperature at a constant level over a wide range of environmental temperatures. Many other animals, for example fish, amphibians and reptiles as well as the invertebrates, cannot do this. Their body temperature is always very close to the environmental temperature.

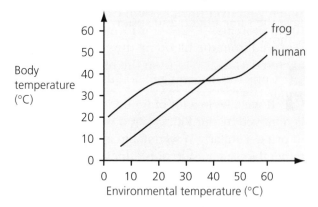

a What is the body temperature of a person and a frog at an atmospheric temperature of 20 °C?
b From the graph, at what external temperature does the human core temperature become dangerously low? Why is it dangerous?
c At what external temperature does the human core temperature become dangerously high? Why is it dangerous?
d Explain how a person maintains a constant core body temperature as the external temperature falls.
e Explain how a person maintains a constant core body temperature as the external temperature rises.

13 Bad maintenance

1 Copy and complete the following sentences. Use the words below to fill the gaps.

addicted bodies withdrawal symptoms alcohol

Drugs we use for pleasure affect our .... and change the way we feel. Even very common drugs like .... and tobacco, which can be used legally by adults, can harm our bodies and even kill us.

Drugs change the chemical processes in people's bodies, so we often become .... to them. We need more and more of the drug to have the same effect, and suffer .... without them.

2 Copy the diagram and add the labels below.

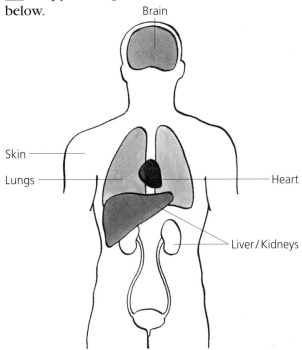

A Affected and damaged by all drugs – can gradually lose control.

B Damaged as they have to remove drugs from the blood – they cannot always cope.

C Damaged by smoking and solvent abuse.

D Damaged by solvent abuse. Smoking causes it to age more rapidly by cutting down the oxygen supply.

E Affected by smoking as it is harder to pump blood around the body and blood carries less oxygen.

3 The diagram shows the incidence of cigarette smoking among American teenagers.

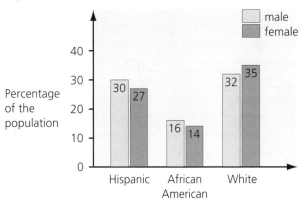

a In which group of American teenagers do the highest percentage smoke?

b What is the main difference in the smoking patterns of the Hispanic and African American youngsters compared with the white group?

c How would you expect these figures to affect the lung cancer figures in the future?

d What are the main negative effects of smoking on
  i your heart
  ii your blood
  iii your lungs?

e When the dangerous effects of smoking are so well known, why do you think young people start smoking?

f Why do people of all ages carry on smoking once they have started?

4 **a** Why does drinking even a small amount of alcohol increase your risk of being involved in a road accident
  i as a driver
  ii as a pedestrian?

b Some people argue that it should be illegal to drink any alcohol and then drive a car. What do you think? Explain your reasons.

14 What a life you lead!

In theory, every baby is born with an equal chance in life. In practice we know this isn't true. The part of the world you are born in, the parents you are born to, whether you are female or male - all of these things and many more affect how your life will turn out.

1 **Sara** is a girl born in the UK in the 1990s. Her mother is bringing Sara and her older brother Jason up on her own. She works at a local shop and is usually home from work by 6 o'clock in the evening, although sometimes she has to work until 10 o'clock.

There isn't always enough to eat so Sara often goes to school without any breakfast. Her mother doesn't like to claim free school meals so Sara often only eats once a day. Her teachers complain that she doesn't concentrate in lessons sometimes.

a List three things which concern you about Sara's life.
b Suggest three ways in which Sara's life could be made healthier or safer.

2 **Chuck** is a teenage boy in America. His parents are very well off but they are both very busy, running a successful business. He has a lot of free time and has lots of money to spend more or less as he likes.

There is always plenty of food in the house, and the family often eats out or sends out for take-aways. Chuck is very overweight and he doesn't like sport because the other kids often laugh at him. His ideal afternoon is playing computer games or watching videos with his mates whilst eating lots of snack food and drinking cola.

a What are the biggest health problems in Chuck's life?
b What could Chuck (or his parents) do to improve the situation?

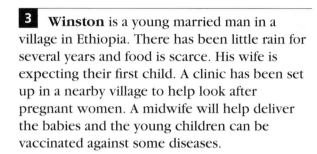

3 **Winston** is a young married man in a village in Ethiopia. There has been little rain for several years and food is scarce. His wife is expecting their first child. A clinic has been set up in a nearby village to help look after pregnant women. A midwife will help deliver the babies and the young children can be vaccinated against some diseases.

Winston is keen for his wife to go to the clinic, but her mother wants her to do things the traditional way without leaving the village.

a Why do you think Winston's mother-in-law wants her daughter to have her baby in the traditional way?
b What health advantages does Winston think going to the clinic will give his wife and child?

4 **Elsie** is an elderly woman living in the UK. Her husband has died after 50 years of marriage. She has her own home and is still relatively fit and well, but doesn't always want to cook meals just for herself.

She has always enjoyed lots of exercise but isn't sure about going swimming or walking on her own. She worries about the cost of heating her home and wonders if she should move to live nearer her son and his wife.

a What are the main health concerns for older people like Elsie?
b How could Elsie improve things for herself whilst carrying on living alone?
c If she moved to live near her son and daughter-in-law what might be
  i the advantages
  ii the disadvantages?

1 Copy and complete the following sentences. Use the words below to fill the gaps.

reproducing   environment   adapted habitat

Animals and plants are usually well _____ to survive in their normal _____ . This means they have features which make sure they are successful at finding food, growing and _____ in a particular location. The place where an animal or plant lives is called its

_____ .

2 Physical factors, for example temperature and availability of water, affect organisms. Copy out these headings.
• Temperature   • Availability of water
• Availability of oxygen or carbon dioxide
• Amount of light

Put each of the following sentences under the correct heading.

A Dormice hibernate all through the winter to help them avoid the cold weather.
B Trout are only found in clean streams with plenty of oxygen in the water.
C Many desert plants flower within hours of a fall of rain.
D Chrysanthemums only flower when there are more than 10 hours daylight per day.
E If there isn't much rainfall and ponds and ditches do not fill with water then the frog population will fall as they cannot lay their spawn.
F Many flowers only open their petals when the temperature reaches a certain level.
G As the day length increases in the spring many birds begin their courtship rituals.
H The carbon dioxide levels in greenhouses may be artificially raised to ensure the plants grow as fast as possible.

3 For each of the organisms shown suggest how the features mentioned below adapt the animal or plant to its habitat.

a Arctic hare: habitat – the Arctic.
   i Eyes for all round vision.   **ii** Sensitive ears.
   iii Thick fur which turns white in winter.
b Cactus: habitat – hot deserts.
   i Thick stem full of water storage cells.
   ii Deep roots.
   iii Leaves reduced to thin spines.

4 Swallows, starlings and fieldfares are all British birds. Use the information from the table to help you answer these questions.

	Swallow	Starling	Fieldfare
Season in the UK	April to October	all year	September to April
Food	insects, mainly caught on the wing	insects, grubs, fruit – a wide variety	berries, worms and grubs
Breeding season	May to August	April to June	May to July

a Which of these birds breed in the UK?
b When swallows are not in the UK they spend their time in South Africa. Why do you think they migrate to Africa in October?
c Why do starlings stay in the UK all year round?
d Fieldfares fly to Northern Europe and Russia when they are not in Britain. Why do you think they might spend the winter months in the UK?

5 Here is some information about living organisms and their habitats. Take each point in turn and explain it in terms of competition between organisms.

a In a British woodland, the ground is covered in a mass of flowers in the early spring. During the summer the trees are in full leaf and the woodland floor is often relatively bare.
b Tawny owls raise their chicks in woodland trees. Once the young are old enough to hunt successfully for themselves the parent birds drive them out.
c Rosebay willowherb is a colonising plant. It forms many seeds, each of which has a fluffy parachute which makes sure it floats a long way away on the breeze.

29

1 Match each word to its definition and then copy them out.

Community a group of organisms of the same species living in an area.

Predators all of the living organisms that share a habitat.

Prey animals that kill and eat other animals.

Population animals that are eaten by other animals.

2 Copy and complete the following sentences. Use the words below to fill the gaps.

**consumers   producers   plants
secondary consumers   animals
primary consumers**

.... can make their own food using energy from the Sun so they are known as ....
All of the .... in the community rely, either directly or indirectly, on the plants for their food – they are .... Animals which eat plants are called .... and animals which eat other animals are ....

3 In a community the number of animals of a particular species is usually limited by the amount of food available.

Wrens are the smallest British bird and live in Britain all year round. They eat small insects and their larvae, spiders and a few small seeds. In 1963 there was a particularly harsh winter, with snow and ice all over the country lasting for weeks. The graph shows the effect this had on the wren population.

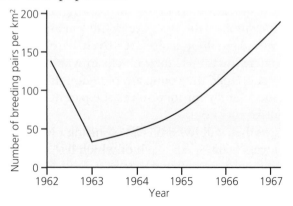

a How many breeding pairs of wrens per km² would you have found in 1962?
b How many breeding pairs of wrens per km² were there in 1963?
c Why do you think the wren population fell like this?
d How long did it take the wren population to recover?

4 The graph shows the number of snowshoe hares and lynxes in Canada between 1845 and 1935. Lynxes prey on snowshoe hares.

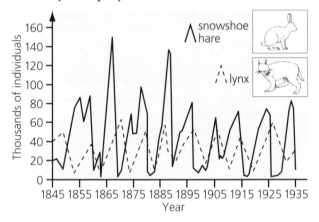

a What happens to the snowshoe hare population each time the lynx population peaks?
b Why does this happen?
c This data seems to show that the link between the two populations is very strong. However, other data on snowshoe hares in an area with no lynxes showed a very similar pattern of rise and fall. What else do you think might be the cause of these changes?

5 Early in the twentieth century rabbits were a major pest to farmers and gardeners alike. There were so many rabbits that they did great damage to growing crops. Then a rabbit disease, myxomatosis, was introduced deliberately into the population. Almost all rabbits were killed by the disease and the rabbit population plummeted.

Explain the effects this would have on the populations of other plants and animals.

1 Copy and complete the following sentences. Use the words below to fill the gaps.

energy photosynthesis animals food chains producer

All living things need .... Plants capture energy from the Sun and use it in .... to make food.

Animals get their energy by eating plants or other .... show us which organisms eat other organisms, and they always begin with a .... (a green plant).

2 Here are five jumbled food chains. Copy each of them out in the correct order.

a stoat $\longrightarrow$ primrose $\longrightarrow$ rabbit
b water fleas $\longrightarrow$ stickleback (small fish) $\longrightarrow$ tiny water plants $\longrightarrow$ pike (big fish)
c cow $\longrightarrow$ grass $\longrightarrow$ human
d tiny sea plants $\longrightarrow$ penguin $\longrightarrow$ fish $\longrightarrow$ polar bear
e blue tit $\longrightarrow$ aphid $\longrightarrow$ ladybird $\longrightarrow$ rose bush

3 The diagram shows a number of interconnected food chains from the Arctic tundra. Use it to help you answer the questions at the top of the next column.

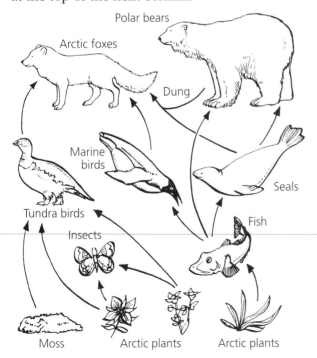

a What do we call a number of interconnected food chains?
b Which organisms are the producers in this system? Why are they so important?
c Which organisms are the primary consumers?
d Which organisms are the secondary consumers?
e Draw three food chains which make up part of this interconnected system.
f Why does a system like this give a much better picture of the real situation than a simple food chain would do?

4 Read the sentences below and use them to help you answer the questions.

The number of organisms at each stage of a food chain can be shown as a pyramid. The size of each block in the pyramid represents the number of organisms. This is called a pyramid of numbers.

a Draw a pyramid of numbers for these two food chains
  i clover $\longrightarrow$ rabbit $\longrightarrow$ fox
  ii tiny water plants $\longrightarrow$ water flea $\longrightarrow$ stickleback
b Why are plants always at the base of these pyramids?
c Why are there fewer organisms at each level of these pyramids?

5 **a** Draw a pyramid of numbers for this food chain: rosebush $\longrightarrow$ aphids $\longrightarrow$ ladybirds $\longrightarrow$ birds

b The diagram shows the food chain from part **a** as a pyramid of biomass. What is a pyramid of biomass?

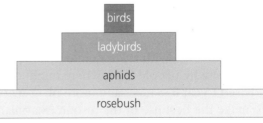

c Using the example in parts **a** and **b**, explain the advantage of using a pyramid of biomass rather than a pyramid of numbers to show the feeding relationships in a food chain.

1 At each stage of a food chain, less material and less energy are contained in the biomass of the organisms.

a Explain how the energy/biomass is used by the organisms in a food chain.

b Explain what happens to the energy which is not transferred from one level to another.

2 The diagram shows a pyramid of biomass.

1.5	large carnivores (large fish)
11	small carnivores (fish, invertebrates)
37	herbivores (turtles, fish, invertebrates)
809	plants

(values give g dry biomass per m²)

a Calculate the percentage biomass passed on
  i from producers to primary consumers
  ii from primary to secondary consumers
  iii from secondary consumers to the top carnivores.

b In any food chain or food web, the biomass of the producers is much larger than that of any other level of the pyramid. Why is this?

c In any food chain or food web there are only a small number of top carnivores. Use your calculations from part **a** to help you explain why.

d All of the animals in the pyramid of biomass shown above are cold blooded. What difference would it have made to the average percentage of biomass passed on between the levels if mammals and birds had been involved? Explain your answer.

3 The world population is increasing and there are food shortages in many areas of the world. Explain, with reference to pyramids of biomass, why people everywhere might be well advised to eat less meat and more plant material to make the best use of the resources available.

4

Chickens for meat and eggs – benefits...	
Intensive farming	**'Free range' farming**
• lots of chickens in small space	• chickens live more natural life
• little or no food wastage	• no heating/lighting costs
• energy wasted in movement/heat loss kept to a minimum	• less food needs supplying as they find some for themselves
• maximum weight gain/number of eggs laid, so cheap eggs/chicken meat	• can charge more money for free range eggs/chickens

Chickens for meat and eggs – costs...	
Intensive farming	**'Free range' farming**
• chickens unable to behave naturally – may be debeaked, etc.	• chickens more vulnerable to weather and predators
• large barns need heating and lighting	• more land needed for each bird
• chicken's legs may break as bones unable to carry weight of rapidly growing body	• eggs cannot be collected automatically
• risk of disease with many birds closely packed	

Produce a leaflet to be handed out in your local shopping centre supporting either intensive farming methods or free range farming methods. In each case back up your arguments with scientific reasoning.

5 *Removing nature's waste*

1   Copy and complete the following sentences. Use the words below to fill the gaps.

**leaves recycled droppings nutrients
microbes decomposed**

Many trees shed their .... every year. Most animal produce .... at least once a day and all plants and animal eventually die.

This dead plant and animal material is .... (broken down) by other organisms, most importantly .... As a result, ... are returned to the soil and can be used again by plants. The same material is .... again and again.

2   Copy the diagram which shows how plants and animals are recycled by microbes. Use the labels below on your diagram.

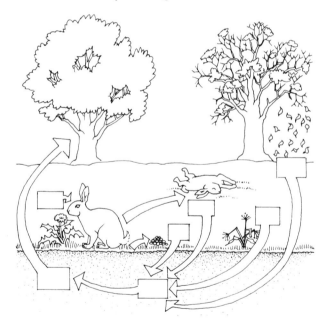

A Plants need nutrients from the soil to grow.
B Droppings, fallen leaves, dead animals and plants are broken down into simple chemicals by the decomposers.
C Animals die.
D Animals produce droppings.
E Plants lose their leaves.
F Plants die.
G Animals eat plants.

3   **a** The temperature in the middle of a compost heap or manure heap will be quite warm because heat is produced as microbes work. How does this help the compost to be broken down more quickly?
b In sewage works oxygen is bubbled through the big tanks containing human sewage and microbes. How does this help to make sure that the human waste is broken down completely?

4   If farmers and gardeners let their crops rot down and ploughed them back into the soil, as you can see on this diagram, the soil would stay full of nutrients and would be very fertile. The problem is there wouldn't be any food to eat!

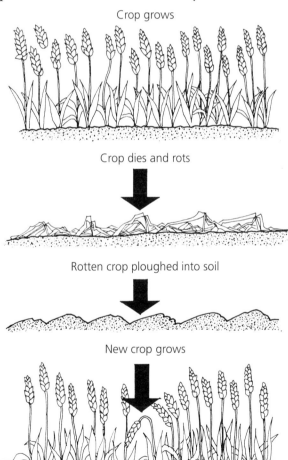

Crop grows

Crop dies and rots

Rotten crop ploughed into soil

New crop grows

Draw and label a diagram to show what really happens to the crops in a farmer's field. Show how nutrients are replaced in the soil.

1 Copy and complete the following sentences. Use the words below to fill the gaps.

respiration   carbon dioxide   decomposed photosynthesise

Plants and animals release energy from carbohydrates in the process of .... They release carbon dioxide into the air as a waste product.

When plants .... they use carbon dioxide from the air. When plants and animals die their bodies are .... by microbes, releasing carbon dioxide into the air.

Carbon dioxide is produced when fuels like wood, coal, gas and petrol burn. So carbon in the form of .... is constantly being taken out of or put into the air.

2 Oxygen and carbon dioxide are constantly produced and used in photosynthesis and respiration.

Copy and complete the diagram to show how this happens.

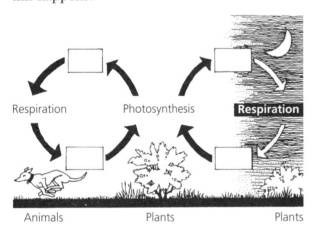

Respiration   Photosynthesis   **Respiration**

Animals   Plants   Plants

3 Copy the diagram of the carbon cycle from the top of the next column. Use the labels A–D on your diagram.

A Photosynthesis: plants remove carbon dioxide from the air and store the carbon in the food they make.
B Respiration: animals give off carbon dioxide as they release the energy from their food.

C Respiration: plants give off carbon dioxide as they release the energy from their food.
D Decay: carbon dioxide is released by microbes which decompose dead animals, dead plants and animals droppings.

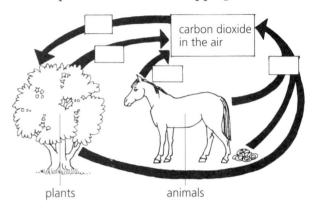

carbon dioxide in the air

plants   animals

4 The graph shows the concentration of carbon dioxide gas in the atmosphere.

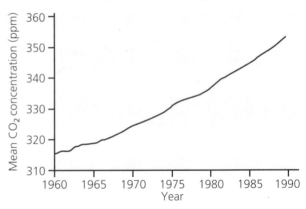

a What happened to the levels of carbon dioxide in the atmosphere from 1960 to 1990?
b One possible cause of this is the increase in the amount of fossil fuels used by people. What is a fossil fuel?
c What is produced when a fossil fuel burns?
d Why has our use of fossil fuels gone up so much?
e Over the same period of time people have cut down enormous areas of forest all over the surface of the Earth. How might this affect the levels of carbon dioxide in the air?

1 Copy and complete the following sentences. Use the words below to fill the gaps.

**dissolved   water   carbon dioxide
respiration   photosynthesis**

Animals and plants which live in .... need oxygen and produce .... in just the same way as organisms which live on the land.

Pond animals and plants use oxygen .... in the pond water for .... As they respire they release carbon dioxide which dissolves in the water. This dissolved carbon dioxide is then used by water plants for ....

2 a Creatures can be divided into various groups. Match each group to the examples given and then copy them out.

Producers	animals like water boatmen and great diving beetles which eat other animals.
Herbivores	organisms like the waterlouse and various microbes which feed on decaying plant and animal remains.
Carnivores	green water plants use the energy in sunlight to make food.
Decomposers	animals like the pond snail which feed on pond weed and other water plants.

b Make a list of the organisms from part **a** which produce carbon dioxide.
c Make a list of the organisms from part **a** which use carbon dioxide.

3 A doctors' surgery decided to install a fish tank to liven up a dark corner of their waiting room. They put five fish and a number of water plants into the tank. However, they had a number of problems in keeping the fish alive. Explain what happened in each case.

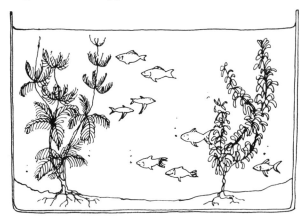

a The first five fish all died.
b A light was put in the tank and five more fish were added. These fish all survived.
c One of the doctors brought another six fish and put them into the tank. Within a few days they started to die.
d A patient brought in a small bubble pump which pumped air into the water and no more fish died, even when a patient brought another new one in.
e Green algae started to grow all over the surface of the glass, making it difficult to see into the tank. What organisms could be added to the tank to help prevent this problem?

1 **a** Why is nitrogen so important in living organisms?

b Some plants, such as beans and clover, have special nodules on their roots which contain bacteria. These bacteria can capture and 'fix' nitrogen from the air in a form which can be used by the plants. Why is this such an advantage for these plants?

2 Copy and complete the labelling of this diagram of the nitrogen cycle. Show clearly the role of microbes and detritus feeders in this cycle.

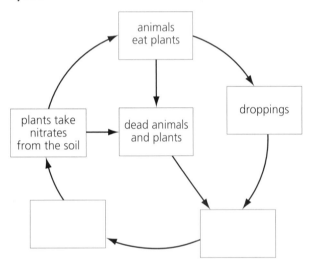

3 One of the most important developments of the 18th century Agrarian Revolution in Britain was 'Turnip' Townsend's idea of three-field crop rotation.

His idea was that each field should be planted on a three-year rotation to improve crop yields. One year in every three the field should be rested (lie fallow). It would be just planted with clover which would then be ploughed in. His idea proved very successful and people grew much more food as a result.

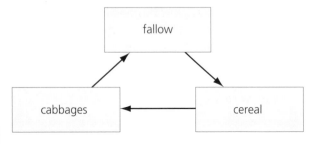

Explain, using your knowledge of soil nutrients and the nitrogen cycle, why this crop rotation improved soil fertility. In particular, what was the importance of the fallow year?

4 The diagram shows what happened to the nitrate and oxygen levels in a stream close to a large arable farm after a particularly wet spring.

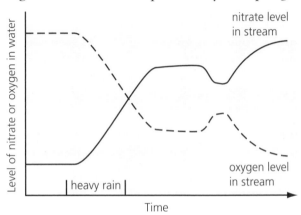

a Why did the nitrate levels in the stream rise so noticeably?

b What would you expect to happen to the plant population of the stream as a result of this rise?

c How would you explain the dip in the nitrate level followed by another rise?

d What would you expect to happen to the microbe population of the stream?

e How is this related to the change in the oxygen level in the water?

f What effect would these changes have on the fish population of the stream?

g What is this type of pollution called?

h Why would it be very difficult to find out who was to blame for the pollution?

9 Polluting the environment

1 Copy and complete the following sentences. Use the words below to fill the gaps.

pollution   organisms   environment

The world we live in contains many different .... which depend on each other and the .... around them to stay alive. Human activities may disturb the environment, causing damage to living organisms – this is ....

2 We pollute the world in which we live in lots of ways. Examples include pumping sewage into the sea, burying radioactive waste on the land and letting factories produce toxic fumes. Copy and complete the table to show ways in which people pollute the world. Try to think of as many examples as possible.

Area polluted	How do we pollute it?
water	
air	
land	

3

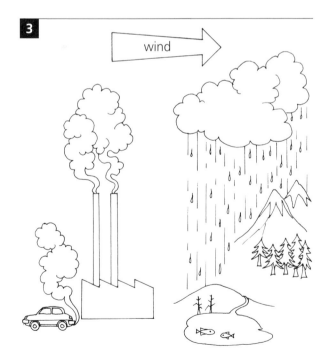

Copy the diagram (at the bottom of the previous column) which shows how acid rain is formed. Use the labels below on your diagram.

A When fossil fuels are burned in cars or power stations carbon dioxide, sulphur dioxide and nitrogen dioxide are released.
B The gases may be blown in the wind to other areas or even other countries.
C The gases dissolve in the rain and make it strongly acidic.
D Acid rain damages trees directly, stripping the leaves and killing the plants.
E Acid rain damages water life indirectly. The water in lakes and rivers becomes acidic and this in turn kills plants and animals alike.

4 The table contains some data about the production of sulphur dioxide in a number of European countries in the late 1980s.

Country	Sulphur dioxide emitted (kg / person / year)
Hungary	153
Finland	119
Spain	99
Italy	90
Britain	83
Poland	76
Sweden	60
Netherlands	31
Switzerland	18

a Draw a bar chart to show the data more clearly.
b Which two countries are the highest producers of sulphur dioxide?
c Which two countries produce the least sulphur dioxide?
d Poland and Sweden are not the highest producers of sulphur dioxide, yet both countries have suffered enormous damage from acid rain. Explain how this can happen.
e How might countries cut back on the amount of sulphur dioxide they produce? Think of as many ways as you can.

1 Copy and complete the following sentences. Use the words below to fill the gaps.

**damaging   local   pollution   organisms
human   population**

Human activities can have a big effect on the life of all other _____ . The effect may be positive (for good) or it may be _____ . When the _____ population of the Earth was much smaller, the effects of human activity were usually relatively small and _____ . But the rapid growth of the human _____ and increased living standards mean that the negative effects of _____ can affect the whole planet.

2 People affect animal and plant populations in lots of ways, and they don't all involve pollution. Read the following passage and use it to help you answer the questions at the top of the next column.

Years ago sailors landed on Abingdon Island in the Galapagos Archipelago. Abingdon Island was home to a particular type of giant tortoise. These are very large, slow-growing reptiles which can live for over a hundred years and do not breed for many years after hatching.

While the sailors were on the island, some of the goats belonging to the sailors escaped. Goats are large mammals with big appetites. They breed relatively quickly.

Over the years the growing goat population ate so many of the plants which had made up the food of the giant tortoises that the reptiles could not cope with the competition. In the 1960s they became extinct on Abingdon Island. The goats still live there.

a Give three reasons why goats were so successful on Abingdon Island.
b Give three reasons why the tortoises could not compete with the goats.
c Draw a simple graph to show what happened to the population of
  i the goats
  ii the food plants
  iii the tortoises
  on the island from the time the goats escaped to the time the tortoises became extinct.

3 Some time after DDT was introduced as a pesticide, people noticed that the numbers of large fish-eating birds like herons were falling. The tissues of these birds were analysed and were found to contain amounts of DDT which meant they couldn't reproduce properly. The eggs the birds produced had very thin shells which broke too easily for many chicks to survive. All of the animals in the food chain contained DDT, but only the large birds were affected like this.

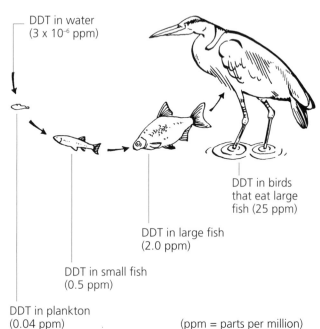

DDT in water
(3×10^{-6} ppm)

DDT in birds that eat large fish (25 ppm)

DDT in large fish (2.0 ppm)

DDT in small fish (0.5 ppm)

DDT in plankton (0.04 ppm)

(ppm = parts per million)

a Explain why the levels of DDT go up in each level of the food chain.
b When new pesticides are developed to be sprayed on our crops, what tests would you like to see carried out to make sure the chemicals are safe.

1 Copy and complete the following sentences. Use the words below to fill the gaps.

**pollution   bathing   sewage   resource
homes   sewage farm**

Water is a valuable .... We use a lot of water in our .... and factories. At home, water is used for activities such as .... , flushing toilets and washing clothes. The dirty water produced is called .... If it was simply pumped into rivers it would cause a lot of .... , but it is carried to a .... where it is treated to make it harmless before flowing into a river or the sea.

2 Rearrange these sentences to describe the way a sewage farm works. Copy the sentences out in the correct order.

• The liquid is now safe to pump into a river or the sea.
• Liquids and semi-solids continue round to the filter bed, where the sewage is sprinkled over a bed of large stones covered with microbes.
• The microbes feed on the sewage and digest it as it trickles through the bed of stones.
• The grit pit traps large objects such as bottles and sticks.
• In the humus tank the remaining solid matter settles out.
• Raw sewage from industry and homes enters the sewage farm.
• Solid matter then settles out as a sludge in the settling tank.

3 When sewage is treated at a sewage farm it is sprinkled over a bed of large stones covered with microbes. Why is this step so important in the production of relatively clean water from a sewage farm?

4 Although sewage farms treat the foul water which reaches them and make it cleaner, the water which is pumped out can still have a very noticeable effect, as shown by the graphs at the top of the next column.

a What happens to the oxygen level in the water below a sewage outfall? Explain this effect.

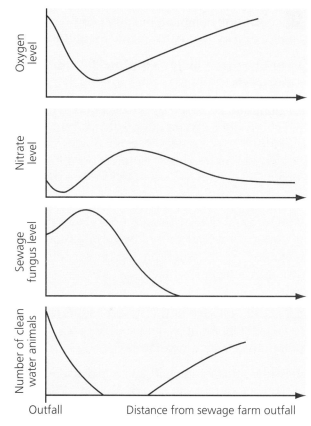

b What happens to the nitrate level in the water below the sewage outfall? Explain this effect.

c Sewage fungi is the name given to some organisms, many of them fungi, which form brown slimes near a sewage outfall. They grow where there is a high level of nitrates and other nutrients, and they can survive in low oxygen levels. Why are they so common near the sewage outfall?

d What happens to the number of clean water animals? Explain this effect.

e If treated sewage is discharged out into the sea rather than into a river, the effects on the environment are usually less obvious. Why is this?

5 Eutrophication is an ecological problem which is particularly associated with sewage getting into rivers and with areas with a lot of agricultural activity.

a Outline the sequence of events in eutrophication.

b Suggest ways in which the problem might be avoided.

1   Copy and complete the following sentences. Use the words below to fill the gaps.

asthma   fossil fuels   sulphur dioxide rainforests

Air pollution is caused by burning .... , which produce carbon monoxide, carbon dioxide, ... and nitrogen dioxide. Cars, power stations and many factories burn fossil fuels.

Cutting down .... removes the trees which would otherwise mop up some of the pollution. Problems caused by air pollution include .... and bronchitis and acid rain damage to the environment.

2   Lead pollution in the air can cause damage to your brain. An important source of lead pollution is from car exhausts.

a Babies and young children are particularly likely to suffer from lead poisoning. Why?
b Traffic police in some large cites wear breathing apparatus when they are on duty. Why do you think this is necessary?

3   The table shows the amounts of various air pollutants in two areas.

| Air pollutant | Amount of air pollutant in micrograms per cubic metre of air... | |
	Area A	Area B
sulphur dioxide	80	25
lead	1300	50
smoke	110	25
nitrogen dioxide	321	119
carbon monoxide	106	33

a Plot a bar graph to show the levels of air pollutants in area A and area B.
b Where could the pollutants have come from?
c Why do you think the levels are so different in area A compared to area B?

4   The table (at the top of the next column) gives figures showing the death rate per 100,000 people from a variety of diseases in different sized communities.

Disease	Rural population	Small town	Medium town	Large town/city
bronchitis	58	77	79	91
pneumonia	42	45	52	58
strokes	155	175	170	155

It is always difficult to prove a link between environmental factors and disease. Data like these are used to try and show whether a link is there or not.

a Which disease would it be easiest to argue shows a link with air pollution?
b There are many things which are different when living in a city compared with living in the country. Why do you think air pollution is the main suspect as the cause of the trend you can see in the number of deaths from both bronchitis and pneumonia?

5   The diagram shows three chimneys, of different height.

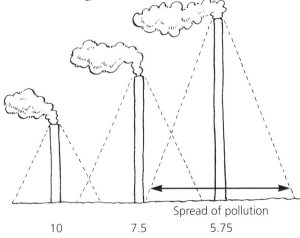

Spread of pollution

| 10 | 7.5 | 5.75 |

Level of pollution under chimney in arbitrary units

a What is the effect of a taller factory chimney on the pollution levels immediately below the chimney?
b What is the other main effect on pollution of using a taller factory chimney?
c The height of the chimney is not the only factor which affects what happens to any smoke pollution which is produced. What else will affect where the smoke goes?

1 The diagram shows some of the main causes of global warming.

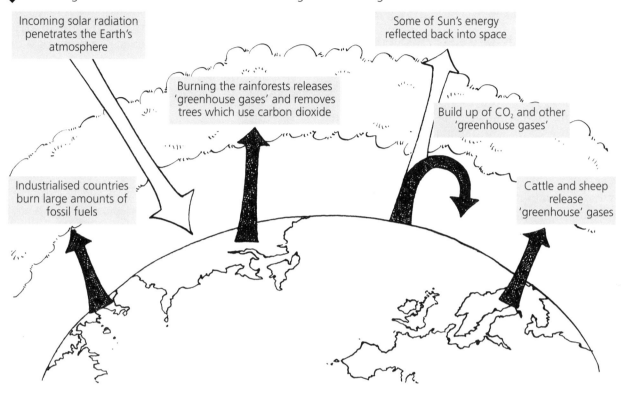

Incoming solar radiation penetrates the Earth's atmosphere

Some of Sun's energy reflected back into space

Burning the rainforests releases 'greenhouse gases' and removes trees which use carbon dioxide

Build up of CO₂ and other 'greenhouse gases'

Industrialised countries burn large amounts of fossil fuels

Cattle and sheep release 'greenhouse' gases

Many scientists are concerned about global warming. They can produce evidence which suggests that human activities are affecting the temperature of the Earth, an effect which could be disastrous for us all.

Other scientists think the problem is not so serious. Many ordinary people are confused by all the different stories they hear.

Using the information in the diagram above, produce an article for your local paper on global warming to help ordinary people understand the issues. Explain what global warming is, how it is caused and what it might mean for the future of the planet.

2 A conventional power station only converts about 30% of its fuel energy into electrical energy. The rest is lost as waste gases and heat energy.

However, in a number of cities this 'wasted' heat is being put to good use. Instead of individuals buying fuel to heat their own homes, much of the heat produced in a power

station is used to provide hot water for heating and washing to all homes in the area. Combined Heat and Power, or CHP, makes the power stations about 90% efficient, as much of the wasted heat energy is now used. It also reduces the greenhouse gas emissions.

In Woking (in Surrey), the local council has been able to reduce carbon dioxide production by 27% by introducing a CHP plant and by using electricity and other fuels carefully. Local people who are involved in the scheme will save up to £100 a year on their heating and electricity bills.

a Why does CHP reduce the level of carbon dioxide emissions?

b What might be the objections to CHP by individuals?

c We cannot set up local CHP schemes, but we can all affect greenhouse gas emissions on a small scale. Suggest as many ways as possible that you as an individual, as part of your family and school community, might reduce carbon dioxide emissions.

1   Copy and complete the following sentences. Use the words below to fill the gaps.

**population   acid rain   resources
carbon dioxide**

The human .... is increasing all the time. We are using up more of the Earth's .... and producing increasing amounts of waste.Our cars and factories produce .... and other chemicals which cause .... and lung diseases.

2

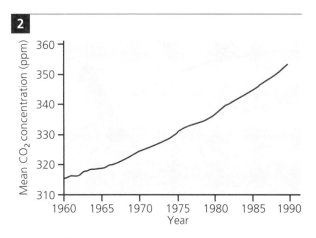

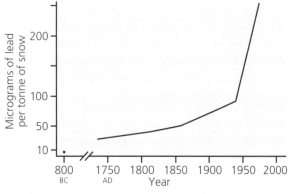

a What has happened to the levels of carbon dioxide in the air over the last 30 years?
b What has happened to the levels of lead measured in the Arctic snow since 1900?
c What single invention could be largely responsible for both of these trends?

3   The Flat Peninsula has a number of different features. Sandy is a seaside town, very quiet in winter but with a large number of visitors in summer. Visitors are attracted by the sandy beaches and the protected woodlands nearby, which contain rare animals and birds. The Field Centre there is popular with schools.

Large container ships sail past the peninsula on their way to a large port further down the coast. Rabbit's Farm is mixed, with cattle and about 250 acres of crops. The River Rab flows past the town of Vermin, the farm and Sandy before reaching the sea. The Pooter Power Station is oil-fired and supplies electricity to the peninsula.

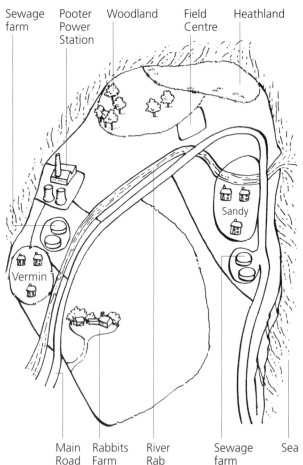

a What do you think will be the main pollution problems in Sandy?
b Last summer, eutrophication was a problem in the River Rab. The problem was monitored as the river flowed past the Field Centre. Suggest what may have led to this problem.
c Make a list of the main possible sources of pollution over the whole peninsula. Choose one source and suggest ways in which the pollution or the problems which result from it might be kept to a minimum.

1 Similarities and differences

1 Copy and complete the following sentences. Use the words below to fill the gaps.

characteristics offspring chromosomes parents genes

Young animals and plants look like their .... They have similar characteristics because of information passed on from parents to .... in the sex cells from which they have developed.

The information is carried by the .... which make up the .... found in the nucleus of every cell. Different genes control the development of different ....

2 Match the words below to the part they play in reproduction. Copy out the correct pairs.

Nucleus   contains the chromosomes which carry genes from the father.

Sperm   contains the chromosomes carrying thousands of genes.

Egg   contains chromosomes from both parents.

Fertilised egg   contains the chromosomes which carry genes from the mother.

3 **a** If you have tall parents you are likely to be tall. If you have short parents you are likely to be short. What does this tell you about how differences in height occur?
b The graph shows the range of heights seen in normal teenagers now and 100 years ago.

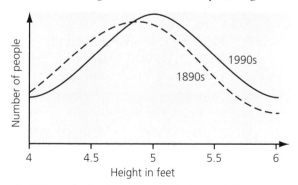

i What might have caused these differences?
ii What does this suggest about the way differences in height occur?

c Some midwives say they can tell how tall a baby will be when it is grown up. What factors do you think will affect its height?

4 The diagram is of a family tree with the eye colour shown.

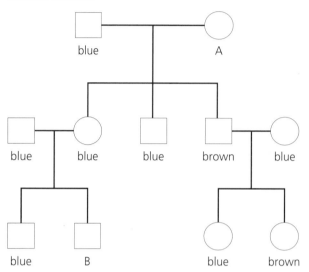

a What eye colour might you find in individuals A and B?
b Copy and complete this table to show three features which are probably passed on from parents to their children and three features which are probably not inherited.

Features inherited	Features not inherited

Chose your features from this list:
- nose shape
- freckles
- liking jazz music
- being musical
- telling lies
- shaved hair
- big feet
- disliking snow
- allergies
- having lots of children.

1 Copy and complete the following sentences about sexual and asexual reproduction, choosing the correct ending in each case.

a The new individual formed in asexual reproduction....

b In sexual reproduction special male and female sex cells fuse (join)....

c The new individual formed in sexual reproduction....

d The special sex cells involved in sexual reproduction....

e A clone is the identical offspring formed....

Choose the endings from:
• ....are known as gametes.
• ....contains a mixture of genetic information from both parents.
• ....to form a unique new cell.
• ....as a result of asexual reproduction.
• ....is identical to the parent.

2

A   B

a How has the small plant shown in diagram A been produced?

b What sort of reproduction is this?

c How were the seeds in diagram B produced?

d How are the new plants which you would grow from the packet of seeds (diagram B) different from the new plant shown in diagram A?

3 The sex of a new human being is decided at the moment of conception.

a How is sex determined in humans?

b The cells in some people show a dark patch inside the cells known as the Barr body (see the diagram at the top of the next column). This shows that one of their two X chromosomes has been deactivated.

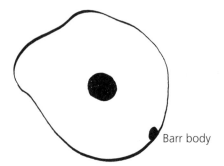

Barr body

A group of young people were tested for the presence of a Barr body for experimental purposes. 20 showed Barr bodies and 24 did not.

i How many of those tested were women?

ii How can you tell?

4 Sometimes identical twins are separated at birth, adopted and brought up in different families. Comparing these genetically identical individuals who have been brought up in different environments with other identical twins brought up together gives us some very useful information. We can then compare them with non-identical twins and ordinary brothers and sisters.

	Difference in...	
Type of sibling	height (cm)	mass (kg)
Identical twins brought up togehter	1.7	1.9
Identical twins brought up apart	1.8	4.5
Non-identical twins	4.4	4.6
Non-twin siblings	4.5	4.7

a Produce bar graphs to show this data clearly.

b Which feature, height or mass, do you think is affected least by the environment identical twins are brought up in? Explain your answer.

c Does the comparison made with non-identical twins and ordinary siblings confirm your answer to part b? Explain why.

d This type of data on identical twins is very useful but quite rare. Why do you think such information is difficult to collect?

1 **a** How many chromosomes are there in a normal human body cell?
b How many chromosomes are there in a human gamete (sex cell)?
c What is the name of the special type of cell division which produces gametes from ordinary body cells?
d Whereabouts in the body would this type of cell division take place?
e Copy the diagram that shows this type of cell division. Label it to explain what is happening at each stage.

2 Once the gametes have fused at fertilisation they form a single cell. This must then divide to produce millions of cells, each with an exact copy of the chromosomes, in order to form a baby. This type of cell division is called mitosis.

a Copy and complete the diagram to show how mitosis happens. You need to add chromosomes, labels and arrows.

          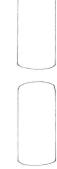

b Why is it so important that exact copies of the chromosomes are made?
c Mitosis is very important during the development of a baby from a fertilised egg. It is also important all through life. Explain why.

3 Explain the roles of the different types of cell division in

a human reproduction
b the production of new plants from cuttings.

4 *Controlling fertility*

1 Copy and complete the following sentences. Use the words below to fill the gaps.

hormone   ovaries   uterus   blood

The monthly release of a fertile egg from a woman's .... and the thickening of the lining of her .... in preparation for pregnancy are controlled by hormones.

A .... is a chemical messenger released in one part of the body and carried in the .... around the body to have its effect on another part.

2 Match each word to its definition and then copy them out.

Ovary where sperm from a man's penis enter the woman's body during sexual intercourse.

Oviduct the organ which supports a developing fetus for 9 months. A blood-rich lining is prepared each month which is shed as the menstrual period if no pregnancy occurs.

Uterus (womb) releases a ripe ovum each month and makes the hormones oestrogen and progesterone which control the menstrual cycle.

Vagina the site where fertilisation of the egg by the sperm takes place.

3 Some of the hormones which control the natural menstrual cycle are used in contraceptive pills to stop eggs leaving the ovary and so prevent pregnancies. Some of the hormones can also be used in fertility drugs to encourage the release of eggs which can help women who find it difficult to get pregnant.

There are risks. Fertility drugs carry a risk of having lots of babies at the same time – they might not all survive. The contraceptive pill carries a slight risk of blood clots forming in the veins, especially in smokers, and this can be life-threatening.

Knowing the risks, people readily carry on with these treatments. Why do you think this is?

4 **a** Copy the diagram of part of the hormone system which controls the female menstrual cycle. Use the labels below on your diagram.

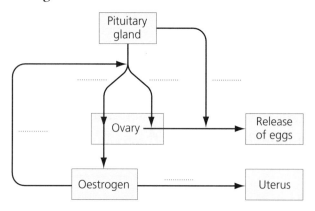

A FSH (follicle stimulating hormone) from the pituitary gland stimulates eggs to mature and ripen in the ovaries.
B FSH also causes the ovaries to make the hormone oestrogen.
C Oestrogen stimulates the womb to develop a blood-rich lining ready for pregnancy.
D Oestrogen stops the production of FSH. As the level of oestrogen rises the level of FSH falls until the egg is released.
E LH from the pituitary gland stimulates egg release.

b If a woman does not produce enough FSH she will be infertile. Explain why.

5 **a** Hormone treatment is often used to help overcome infertility. If follicle stimulating hormone (FSH) is given to help overcome poor ovulation, the dose must be very carefully monitored. Why?

b If a woman has blocked oviducts, it may be necessary to harvest ripe eggs from her ovaries, fertilise them with sperm from her partner outside her body and then implant the tiny developing embryos back inside her uterus (in vitro fertilisation). Some of the embryos may be frozen and saved in case the pregnancy fails or in case the parents want another child later.

i In this sort of treatment a very high dose of FSH will be given. Why?
ii Oestrogen will also be given as the time to harvest the eggs gets nearer. Why is this?

5 Patterns of inheritance

1 Match each word to its definition and then copy them out.

Gene   when both chromosomes in a pair contain different alleles of a gene.

Allele   an allele which controls the development of characteristics only if it is present on both of the chromosomes.

Dominant allele   when both chromosomes in a pair contain the same allele of a gene.

Recessive allele   gene which has different forms.

Homozygous   a unit of genetic information linked to a particular characteristic.

Heterozygous   an allele which controls the development of a characteristic even when it is present on only one of the chromosomes.

2 Whether or not you can roll your tongue is decided by a single gene with two alleles. The 'roller' allele **R** is dominant to the 'non-roller' allele **r**. Use this information to help you answer these questions.

Tom can roll his tongue but Sandy can't. They are expecting a baby.
a What are Sandy's tongue rolling genes? How do you know?
b If the baby can't roll its tongue, what does this tell us about Tom's tongue rolling genes?
c If the baby can roll its tongue, what does this tell us about Tom's tongue rolling genes?

3 Peas are usually round and green, but sometimes they are wrinkled. Peas have a gene controlling their appearance. This gene has two alleles, round and wrinkled. The round allele **W** is dominant to the wrinkled allele **w**.

A gardener has been given a new pea plant which has smooth, round peas. However, before breeding it with her pure breeding smooth, round peas she wants to check the plant is not heterozygous for the wrinkled gene by carrying out a test cross.

a What sort of plant would she need to use to carry out a test cross like this?
b Show the test cross and the results she would get if the new pea plant was
  i homozygous for the round gene
  ii heterozygous for the round gene.

4 Manx cats are born with no tail. If a Manx cat is mated to a normal cat, half the litter will have tails and half will not.

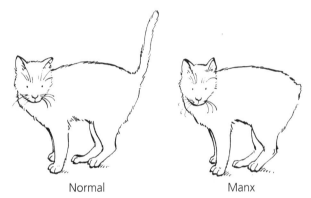

Normal   Manx

This suggests that Manx cats are heterozygous for a dominant gene **T** which causes no tail to form, with the normal tail gene **t** being recessive.

a Show the Manx cat cross described above.

However, when two Manx cats are mated there are always fewer Manx kittens born than you would expect. The homozygous form of the **T** gene is so damaging that the kittens which are homozygous for **T** die before birth.
b Show a cross between two Manx cats. What ratio of Manx kittens to normal kittens would you expect to be born if the homozygous form was not so damaging?
c What ratio of Manx kittens to normal kittens is actually born, and why?

47

1 Copy and complete the following sentences. Use the words below to fill the gaps.

Huntingdon's chorea   carriers   genetic   cystic fibrosis

People inherit _____ diseases from their parents. One of the most common is _____ . It is inherited from both parents who may be _____ of the disease without suffering any effects themselves. Another inherited disease, _____ , is very rare and is passed on from one parent, who develops the disease later in life.

2 Cystic fibrosis and Huntington's chorea are both genetic diseases. Both have devastating effects on the health of a sufferer. One can be managed, the other is still untreatable.

You are given a number of symptoms of these two diseases. Write one paragraph about cystic fibrosis and one about Huntington's chorea, using the relevant symptoms in each paragraph.

- 1 child in every 2000 born in the UK is affected.
- This is an inherited disease of the nervous system.
- In middle age, control over the muscles starts to go.
- The body produces thick sticky mucus which blocks the air passages to the lungs and makes breathing difficult.
- Loss of muscle control is followed by gradual mental deterioration.
- Those affected often get chest infections, which can be treated by antibiotics but can cause permanent damage to the lungs.
- Regular physiotherapy is needed to help keep the chest clear of mucus.

3 **a** Frankie and Annie are planning a family. Frankie's sister has cystic fibrosis, and tests have shown that he is a carrier. Annie has had tests too, and she is not a carrier of the faulty gene. Produce a genetic diagram to show the chance of Annie and Frankie having a child affected by cystic fibrosis.

b Steve and Paula also want to start a family. Neither of them has any cystic fibrosis in their families, but they could be carriers. Produce genetic diagrams to show the different possibilities of them producing a child suffering from cystic fibrosis.

4 Achondroplastic dwarfism is a genetic condition which affects the long bones of the body. As a result, the bones do not grow to normal size, although in every other way affected individuals are quite normal. It is inherited as a dominant gene. Embryos which are homozygous for achondroplastic dwarfism die before birth. Use this family tree to help you answer the following questions.

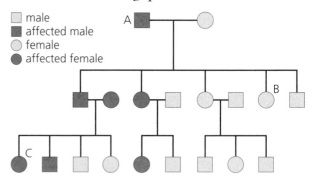

- □ male
- ■ affected male
- ○ female
- ● affected female

a Chose a suitable capital and lower case letter to represent the two alleles. Give the genotype you would expect for individuals A, B and C on the family tree.

b In the family where two people with achondroplastic dwarfism married, one pregnancy ended in miscarriage. What might be the explanation for this? Use a genetic diagram to help you explain.

c Huntington's chorea is inherited in the same way, but affected individuals look quite normal until the symptoms of the disease start to appear in middle age. It is now possible to test people in an affected family for the condition, although there is no treatment available.

  i Do you think this is a useful thing to do?

  ii What difficulties might arise from the tests?

5 **a** What is meant by gene therapy?

b How might it help people affected by inherited diseases like cystic fibrosis and Huntington's chorea?

1 a What is sickle cell anaemia?

b Two people who are heterozygous for sickle cell anaemia have four children, one of whom has severe sickle cell anaemia, one who has normal blood and two who have mild anaemia. Produce a genetic diagram to show this cross.

c People who are heterozygous for sickle cell anaemia have a greatly improved immunity to malaria, a tropical disease which kills about two million people a year. How does this affect which of the children in the family discussed in part b are most likely to live to adulthood

   i if the family live in Africa

   ii if the family live in the UK?

2 a Draw what you would expect the red blood cells to look like for

   i a normal person

   ii a carrier of sickle cell anaemia

   iii a person with sickle cell anaemia.

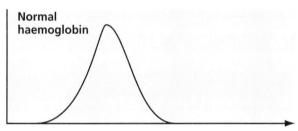

Mass of the haemoglobin molecules

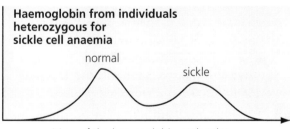

Mass of the haemoglobin molecules

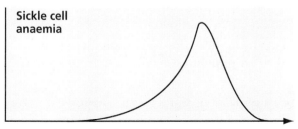

Mass of the haemoglobin molecules

b The graphs in the previous column show the haemoglobin pattern for homozygous normal, heterozygous and homozygous sickle cell anaemia. What does this information tell you about the haemoglobin inside the red blood cells of heterozygous people compared to the haemoglobin in the blood cells of normal people and people with full sickle cell anaemia?

3 When an individual who is heterozygous for sickle cell anaemia is not infected with malaria, most of the red blood cells will look perfectly normal. However, any blood cells which become infected by malarial parasites cannot cope and form the well-known sickle shape. Sickle cells are then broken down and destroyed in the spleen. Blood cells which are not infected continue to keep their normal shape and carry oxygen effectively.

a How do you think this response helps make the body resistant to malaria?

b Thalassaemia is another form of anaemia due to a faulty gene involved in the production of part of the haemoglobin molecule. Heterozygous carriers of the thalassaemia gene also have some resistance to malaria, but homozygous children need to receive regular blood transfusions to keep them alive.

Produce a genetic diagram to show how two heterozygous individuals can produce both a severely affected child and a normal child (**T** is the gene for normal blood, **t** the gene for thalassaemia).

1 Copy and complete the following sentences. Use the words below to fill the gaps.

**characteristics   identical   damp
plastic bags   cuttings**

New plants can be produced quickly and cheaply by taking .... from older plants. These new plants are genetically .... to their parents. This means if cuttings are taken from a plant that has the .... you want, all the cuttings will have them as well.

Cuttings are most likely to grow successfully if they are grown in .... conditions until their roots develop, so they are covered with .... or sheets or put in special propagators.

2 We develop new varieties of animals and plants by choosing organisms which have useful characteristics and breeding from them. The animal or plant may end up looking very different from the original parent. For example, the wheat we use for flour has been selectively bred over thousands of years from wild grasses.

a What do we call breeding animals and plants to get the characteristics we want?
- artificial selection • natural selection
- artificial breeding

b Copy and complete the table of animals and plants which have been artificially selected for particular reasons.

Animal selected	Reason why
hens from wild chickens	i
pigs from wild boar	ii
iii	large milk production
dogs from wolves	iv

Plant selected	Reason why
wheat from wild grasses	'large' ears for food
potatoes from wild potatoes	v
vi	larger, sweeter fruit
garden roses from wild roses	vii

3 The graph shows the increase in world population over the last 10 000 years.

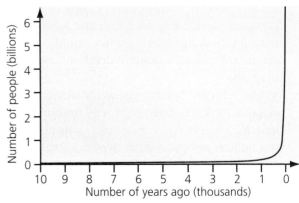

a What is happening to the number of people in the world?
b Why is it so important to increase the yields of many of our crops?
c Many scientists are working hard to produce plants which not only give more and more crops but which are also resistant to disease. Produce a bar chart of the data given in the table which shows the percentage of the total crops lost to disease and pests in 1987.

Crop	% loss
wheat	9.1
maize	9.4
potatoes	21.8
vegetables	10.1
citrus fruit	16.4

Data from Central Statistical Office

d Which crops were most affected by disease?
e Why is increasing resistance to disease as important as increasing the yields of crops?

4 **a** Artificial selection has led to cows which can produce more and more milk. What do you think is the advantage of this?
b Can you think of any disadvantages?
c How would you set about increasing the meat yield of an animal like a pig?

9 High technology breeding

1 Large numbers of identical plants can be grown using micropropagation techniques.

a How does tissue culture differ from traditional methods of taking cuttings?

b Give four advantages of micropropagation over traditional methods of propagation by cuttings.

c Although there are many advantages to these modern techniques, there is also a great disadvantage. The disadvantage is that plants species propagated like this may not survive any major changes in conditions. Why is this?

2 Cloning is no longer a technique used only on plants. Animal clones are now possible too. The arrival of Dolly, the first cloned sheep, caused a considerable stir and the technique continues to be used. Before cloning, animals and plants have usually undergone extensive selective breeding or even genetic engineering to make sure that the clones have only the most desirable genes.

What are the implications of this narrowing of the pool of available genetic information?

3 Every year hundreds if not thousands of sheep and cattle embryos fly through the air being transferred from one country to another. More often than not they are inside the uterus of a rabbit! It is very expensive to transfer large animals about the world, but small ones like rabbits travel easily in crates on planes.

a Once the rabbits reach their destination the embryos are removed and placed inside foster mothers of the right species, where they will grow into normal calves. What is the reason for this transfer?

b Modern techniques mean a single cow may have several hundred calves in one year. How is this possible?

4 Micropropagation techniques mean that, for example, 50 000 new raspberry plants can be produced from one old one, but when using old techniques only two or three new plants would result.

Extracting and cloning embryos from the best bred cows means that they can be genetically responsible for hundreds of calves each year instead of simply two or three at most.

a What are the similarities between cloning plants and cloning animals?

b What are the differences in the techniques for cloning animals and plants?

c Why is there so much interest in finding different ways to make the breeding of farm animals and plants increasingly efficient?

10 Bacterial factories

1 Human growth is usually controlled by the pituitary gland in the brain. If the pituitary gland does not make enough hormone, the child does not grow properly and will remain very small. This condition affects 1 in every 5000 children. Until recently the only way to overcome this condition was to extract growth hormone from the pituitary glands of dead bodies, but it took many bodies to produce enough hormone to enable one child to grow properly. Genetic engineering means that pure growth hormone can now be produced in relatively large amounts by bacteria.

a Copy and label the diagram to explain how a healthy human gene for making growth hormone can be taken from a human chromosome and inserted into a working bacterial cell.

Stage 1

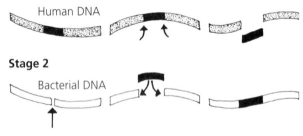

Human DNA

Stage 2

Bacterial DNA

b When children had to be supplied with growth hormone from dead bodies they were exposed to a particular risk. What was it?

c What are the advantages of producing substances such as growth hormone using genetic engineering?

2 a What is the job of insulin in the body?

b Some diabetics can manage their diabetes by careful control of their diet, but about 250 000 people need to inject themselves regularly with insulin several times a day. Since 1922 insulin from pig and cattle pancreases collected from slaughter houses has been used to help diabetics manage their condition. There are several problems with this as a source of insulin. Give two of these problems.

c Genetic engineering has made it possible for bacteria to produce human insulin. In what ways is human insulin from bacteria better for people with diabetes than insulin from animals?

3 Growth hormone is produced to help children whose bodies do not naturally make enough of the hormone.

a Why do you think that parents with short or even average height children might be prepared to pay for growth hormone treatment?

b Some athletes have tried to buy genetically engineered growth hormone. Why do you think they might want it?

c Do you think that either of these uses should be allowed? Give reasons for your answer.

4 Most people are happy to accept the benefits of using engineered bacteria to produce human proteins. More people have concerns about putting human genes into animals like cows, pigs and sheep. Many people are very unhappy at the idea of transplanting organs from an animal such as a pig into a person, even if the organs are genetically 'human'.

a Why do you think people are less concerned about products from bacteria than those formed using sheep and cows?

b What do you think about using organs from other animals in human transplants? Can you think of any other way that the shortage of suitable donor organs might be dealt with?

5 Write a letter to your local newspaper either supporting the introduction and use of new biotechnology or objecting to the introduction and use of biotechnology. Whichever viewpoint you take, support your arguments with facts as far as possible.

11 The code for life

1 The Human Genome Project is an attempt by scientists from all over the world to sequence all of the bases on the human chromosomes. This would give us a map of the human genome, showing us where all the genes – and all the nonsense – are sited.

a Produce a table in which you show as many of the potential benefits and the potential problems arising from a complete knowledge of the human genome as you can think of.

b Make some suggestions as to how we, as a society, could try to make sure that we use the findings of the Human Genome Project only to benefit the human race.

2 DNA is a very complicated molecule made up of two long strands. The strands are held together by molecules called bases. There are only four possible bases in DNA, and they always join together in pairs in a particular way because of their shapes.

Because of this, if we know the structure of one strand of DNA we can always work out the structure of the other (complementary) strand.

E.g. if part of one strand is A - A - G - C - T - A
the complementary strand
will be T - T - C - G - A - T

a Part of a strand of DNA is shown at the top of the next column. Remember the complementary bases and work out the sequence of the complementary strand.

A - T - G - T - T - T - A - C - C - G - A - T -
G - G - G - A - A - C - T - G - A

Each chromosome is made up of long strands of DNA, and this DNA contains all the information needed for an entire organism. The information is carried in the genes, which are sequences of groups of three bases, with each 'triplet' coding for a particular amino acid. When all the amino acids coded for in a gene are joined together they make proteins, and proteins (enzymes) control everything going on in a cell or an organism.

b Break up the longer strand of DNA you were given in part **a** into units of three bases, starting from the left-hand end.

Some time ago the genetic code was worked out. This means you can 'translate' a sequence of three bases into an amino acid. For example, the short strand A - A - G - C - T - A gives us the amino acids lysine-leucine. Not all sequences of three bases translate to give an amino acid. Some give instructions to start or stop reading the DNA sequence.

c Use the table of the genetic code (at the bottom of the page) to help you work out the small protein (peptide) coded for in the DNA strand you were given in part **a**.

TTT	phenylalanine	CTT	leucine	ATT	isoleucine	GTT	valine
TTC	phenylalanine	CTC	leucine	ATC	isoleucine	GTC	valine
TTA	leucine	CTA	leucine	ATA	isoleucine	GTA	valine
TTG	leucine	CTG	leucine	ATG	methionine/start	GTG	valine
TCT	serine	CCT	proline	ACT	threonine	GCT	alanine
TCC	serine	CCC	proline	ACC	threonine	GCC	alanine
TCA	serine	CCA	proline	ACA	threonine	GCA	alanine
TCG	serine	CCG	proline	ACG	threonine	GCG	alanine
TAT	tyrosine	CAT	histidine	AAT	asparagine	GAT	aspartic acid
TAC	tyrosine	CAC	histidine	AAC	asparagine	GAC	aspartic acid
TAA	stop	CAA	glutamine	AAA	lysine	GAA	glutamic acid
TAG	stop	CAG	glutamine	AAG	lysine	GAG	glutamic acid
TGT	cysteine	CGT	arginine	AGT	serine	GGT	glycine
TGC	cysteine	CGC	arginine	AGC	serine	GGC	glycine
TGA	stop	CGA	arginine	AGA	arginine	GGA	glycine
TGG	tryptophan	CGG	arginine	AGG	arginine	GGG	glycine

1 Copy and complete the following sentences. Use the words below to fill the gaps.

genes   mutagens   variety   radiation mutations

New forms of genes arise from changes known as .... in the existing ....

These occur naturally and are important for introducing .... The chance of mutations occurring is increased by exposure to ionising .... and chemicals known as ....

2 Ionising radiation can come from radioactive substances such as uranium, ultraviolet light from the Sun and X-rays.

a When you need to have an X-ray, the parts of your body which are not being X-rayed are covered in lead which absorbs radiation. Why?

b People who work in X-ray departments move into a radiation-proof cubicle when they are using the X-ray machine. The levels of radiation they receive are carefully monitored. Why is so much care taken with people who work with ionising radiation?

3 Cigarette smoke contains a number of carcinogens. These are mutagens which make cells develop in an uncontrolled way.

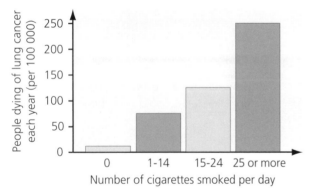

a What effect does smoking cigarettes have on your chance of dying from lung cancer?

b What effect does smoking cigarettes have on the levels of mutagenic chemicals in your body?

c Why does smoking have a particular effect on the incidence of lung cancer?

4 The table shows the effect of an increasing radiation dose on the number of mutations found in cells.

Radiation dose (Grays)	Number of mutations per 100 cells
0.05	1
0.1	2
0.25	6
0.5	11
0.75	18
1.1	28
1.35	32

a Plot a graph of these results, drawing a line of best fit through the points.

b What does the graph show you about the effect of increasing doses of radiation on the rate at which mutations occur?

5 Low doses of radiation may cause mutations to occur in the reproductive cells or in cells anywhere in the body.

Explain carefully the long term implications of

a mutations in the reproductive cells

b mutations in normal body cells.

6 In any population of living organisms, random mutations will cause small changes in the way the body works. The graphs shows how the numbers of resistant insects in a population changed.

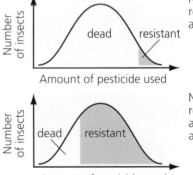

Number of individuals resistant to pesticide after first application

Number of individuals resistant to pesticide after a number of applications

Explain how a pesticide can become ineffective against a type of insect as a result of mutations.

13 Evidence about the past

1 Copy and complete the following sentences. Use the words below to fill the gaps.

extinct evolution billion fossils species rock evidence

The theory of _____ states that all the _____ of living things which exist today, and many others which are now _____ , have evolved from simple life forms which first developed more than three _____ years ago.

Some of the _____ to support this theory comes from _____ , which are the remains of animals and plants from millions of years ago preserved in _____ .

2 Millions of species of animals and plants, like the dinosaurs Rhamphorhyncus, T. Rex and Stegosaurus, have long been extinct. Modern animals and plants are still becoming extinct, often for the same reasons as organisms of old. However, more modern species do have extra problems to deal with. What are they?

3 In a display of prehistoric life three fossils are on display to show three of the different ways in which fossils can form. One was a fossil Icthyosaur skeleton found in layers of rock in Dorset, one was an amber fossil, with small insects trapped intact in the amber, and the last was a rare ice fossil, where part of a mammoth had been found intact in the ice, with the hair and skin preserved.

Take each of these fossils in turn and explain how it was formed many millions of years ago.

4 a The table below shows some of the evolutionary stages of an animal. Which animal is it?

b The table at the bottom of the page shows one of the best fossil records that we have.

Look carefully at the size of each of these animals and at the shape and arrangement of the foot. You also have some information about where we think each of these animals lived. Use this evidence to build up your own theory of how each of these animals lived, and why its feet changed in the way that they did.

Table for **Q4**

	Height (ground to shoulder)	Body shape	Leg bones (digits numbered)	Habitat and leg shape
i	up to 1.6 m		3	Adapted to life in dry grasslands. Very efficient at running. Hoof formed from end of digit 3. Digit 3 lengthened.
ii	1.0 m		3	Increased reliance on speed. Digits 2 and 4 very much reduced. Hoof formed from end of digit 3. Digit 3 thickened for support.
iii	up to 1.0 m		4 — 2, 3	Very dry conditions: prairies. Speed more important. Digits 2 and 4 reduced. Digit 3 used for running – increased in length.
iv	up to 0.6 m		4 — 2, 3	Dry conditions: forests and prairies. Speed important to escape enemies. Only three digits very obvious. Digit 3 much enlarged.
v	about 0.4 m		5, 4 — 2, 3	Size of fox. Lived on soft ground near streams. Four digits in forelimb and three in hindlimb for support on soft ground.

14 Natural selection in action

1 Ptarmigans are birds, members of the grouse family, which are found in Scotland. Their summer plumage is a mixture of browns and cream, but after the autumn moult the feathers of most of the birds grow back almost white. A relatively small number of ptarmigans keep their normal brown and cream colouring.

a How is it possible for the winter plumage of different members of the same species of bird to be so different?

b Is there likely to be a disadvantage in having brown feathers during a Scottish winter?

c Do you think that having white feathers in the winter increases the breeding chances of those ptarmigans which change colour?

d Does the fact that the majority of ptarmigans now have white plumage in winter confirm your hypothesis?

2 One year oyster fishermen in Malpeque bay in Canada noticed a few of the oysters they were catching were diseased, being small and having pus-filled blisters. The graph below shows the subsequent effect of this disease on the oyster population in that area.

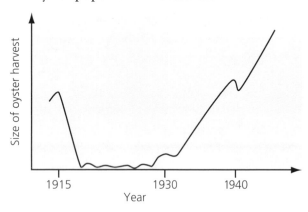

a The first diseased oysters were noticed in 1915. How long did it take for the oyster harvest to be virtually wiped out?

b In which year did the harvest really start to pick up again?

c How long was it before the oyster numbers returned to their 1914 levels?

d Explain what happened in Malpeque Bay in terms of natural selection.

3 It was Charles Darwin who first developed the idea of natural selection as the driving force behind evolution. The finches he studied on the Galapagos Islands were one of the organisms which led him towards this idea. On the mainland of South America there is only one type of finch. Yet on the tiny Galapagos Islands there are six main types of finch and thirteen separate species. They live on different islands or on different parts of the same island.

- Large ground finches (original type from mainland) are coastal and use their short, straight beaks for crushing seeds.

- Lowland cactus ground finches use long, slightly curved beaks with a split tongue to feed on the nectar of the prickly pear cactus.

- Vegetarian tree finches eat soft fruit/buds in the forest using their curved and parrot-like beaks.

- Warbler finches live in the forest catching insects in flight with their slender beaks.

- Woodpecker finches live in forests. They have large, straight beaks and eat insect larvae.

Use the theory of natural selection to explain carefully how this variety might have come about.

1 Sort the following substances into two groups: metals and non-metals.

**tin   polythene   iron   copper   wood
carbon   steel   paper   zinc   magnesium
polystyrene   marble   oxygen   lead
bronze   gold   glass**

2 Copy and complete the table to make a list of places that metals are used around the home.

Metal	Where and why used

3 Copy and complete the following sentences. Use the words below to fill the gaps.

**air   ores   reactive   properties   salt
bases   water**

Metals have many _____ that make them useful. Many metals react with other substances such as _____ and _____ . Because of this, most metals are found combined with other elements; they are then known as

_____ .

The method used to extract the metal depends on how _____ it is. Some metal compounds react with acids – they are called _____ . When an acid reacts with a base, a _____ is formed.

4 The table shows the properties of some metals. (The tensile strength of a material is a measure of how strong it is under tension – when two ends of a piece of it are pulled apart.)

Metal	Density (g/cm³)	Melting point (°C)	Tensile strength
aluminium	2.7	660	70
copper	8.9	1084	130
gold	18.9	1064	78
iron	7.9	1540	211
lead	11.3	327	16
mercury	13.6	-39	–
sodium	0.97	98	low
tungsten	19.4	3410	411

a Which metal is
   i most dense
   ii least dense
   iii strongest?
b Which metal is a liquid at room temperature?
c Why is tungsten used as the filament in electric light bulbs?
d Miniature figures (such as toy soldiers) used to be made from lead. Why?
e A lump of gold is dropped into some mercury. Will it float or sink? Explain your answer.

2 Metals and non-metals

1   Copy and complete the following sentences. Use the words below to fill the gaps.

non-metals   properties   high   low insulators   elements

Everything is made up of simple building blocks called .... Their .... can be used to sort them into groups. One way of sorting is into metals and .... Most metals have .... melting and boiling points. Non-metals have .... melting and boiling points. Metals are conductors of electricity, while non-metals are ....

2   The diagram shows a circuit that could be used for testing the electrical conductivity of samples of materials.

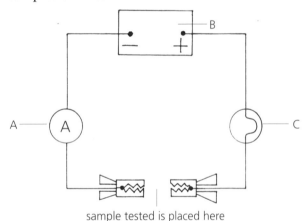

sample tested is placed here

a Copy the diagram. Use the labels below on your diagram.

ammeter   battery   bulb

b Copy and complete the following table.

Substance	Behaviour of bulb
lead	lights up
sulphur	
polythene	
aluminium	
marble	
zinc	
glass	

3   Look at the picture below. Copy the table and use it to make a list of the metals and non-metals you can see. Describe carefully why you think that material has been chosen in preference to others. One example has already been done for you.

Object	Material used	Why used
car body	steel (contains iron)	easily shaped, strong

4   Copy the table with the descriptions of some elements. Decide if each one is a metal or a non-metal. Write down your decision, together with your reasons.

Description of element	Metal or non-metal
yellow solid, melting point 113 °C, brittle, non-conductor of electricity.	**a**
silver liquid, melting point -39 °C, conductor of electricity.	**b**
green gas, boiling point -35 °C.	**c**
yellow solid, melting point 1064 °C, easily shaped, conductor of electricity.	**d**

1 Copy and complete the following sentences, choosing the correct ending in each case.

a Iron can be separated from other metals....

b Choosing the right metal for a job involves....

c Metals can be mixed together....

d Chromium can be added to iron....

e The thermal conductivity of a metal measures how good it is at....

Choose the endings from:

* ....to form alloys.
* ....to form stainless steel.
* ....using a magnet.
* ....conducting heat.
* ....finding out its properties and its cost.

2 The diagram (at the top of the next column) shows some equipment that can be used to show that different substances conduct heat at different rates. A small ball bearing or marble is fixed to the end of each rod, using candle wax. When the tank is filled with hot water, the marbles gradually drop off one by one.

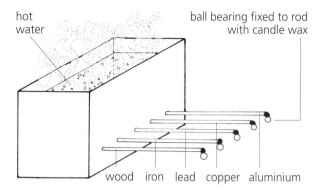

hot water

ball bearing fixed to rod with candle wax

wood   iron   lead   copper   aluminium

Which order do they drop off in? Explain why.

3 Copy and complete the table below of metal alloys, suggesting uses for the alloys from the following list.

* Plugs in automatic sprinkler systems (these melt to allow water out when there is a fire)
* Chemical reactors
* Magnets
* Electric light bulb caps
* Wires giving fixed resistances in electrical instruments

Base your suggestions on the properties of the alloys given in the third column of the table.

Table for **Q3**

Alloy	Composition	Properties	Possible use
Cartridge brass	70% copper, 30% zinc	can be shaped without heating	**a**
Corronel B	66% nickel, 28% molybdenum, 6% iron	very resistant to acids at high temperatures	**b**
Wood's metal	50% bismuth, 13% tin, 27% lead 10% cadmium	melts at about 70 °C	**c**
Cunico	50% copper, 21% nickel, 29% cobalt	easily worked, strongly magnetic	**d**
Constantan	60% copper, 40% nickel	high resistance which does not change greatly with temperature	**e**

1 Copy and complete the following sentences. Use the words below to fill the gaps.

atoms properties compound white reactions

Chemical changes involve chemical .... When the .... of two elements react together, a .... is formed. This may have completely different .... from the elements from which it was formed. For example, at room temperature salt (sodium chloride) is a brittle, ... solid, but sodium is a soft metal and chlorine is a green gas.

2 Copy and complete the following sentences, choosing the correct ending in each case.

a Chemists describe chemical reactions....
b Chemical reactions need energy to be supplied....
c The energy can be supplied....

Choose the endings from:
• ....in the form of heat or electricity.
• ....using equations.
• ....before they will happen.

3 Name the substances formed when the following pairs of substances react together. Write word equations for the reactions.

E.g. iron and oxygen will form iron oxide.
iron + oxygen ⟶ iron oxide

• sodium and oxygen
• zinc and bromine
• iron and chlorine
• hydrogen and fluorine

4 Dynamite is an explosive. It contains atoms of the elements carbon, hydrogen, nitrogen and oxygen. When it explodes, it produces nitrogen gas, carbon dioxide gas, water (as steam) and oxygen.

a Write a word equation for the explosion of dynamite.

The person in the picture is pushing down the plunger of a detonator. This sends an electric current along two wires, which sets off a small explosive charge. This detonates the dynamite, which blows up the building.

b Why must the dynamite be detonated before it will explode?
c Suggest another way of detonating dynamite.
d Why is exploding dynamite so destructive?

5 Several salts called azides are known. Silver azide consists of one atom of silver combined with three atoms of nitrogen. Silver azide is a solid, which explodes when it is hit sharply.

a Suggest *one* possible gas produced when silver azide explodes.
b Energy is required to get a chemical reaction started. Draw a diagram to describe where this energy comes from when some silver azide is detonated by hitting it with a hammer.
c What possible uses has silver azide got?

5 *Metals, air and water*

1 Copy and complete the following sentences, choosing the correct ending in each case.

a Copper metal....
b Gold metal....
c Sodium metal....
d When a metal reacts with air it....
e When a metal reacts with water it....

Choose the endings from:
- ....reacts very quickly with air.
- ....tarnishes slowly in air.
- ....'steals' the oxygen from water, leaving hydrogen.
- ....does not tarnish in air.
- ....combines with the oxygen in the air to form an oxide.

2 Lead and copper have both been used for water pipes (although lead is no longer used as it is poisonous). Why are lead and copper suitable for carrying water, but iron and magnesium are not?

3 Copper is usually used to conduct electricity in wires and cables. However, the contacts in certain switches and in computer equipment use gold. Explain this.

4 Potassium, calcium and zinc all react with oxygen and with water. The products of these reactions are potassium oxide, calcium oxide and zinc oxide for the reactions with oxygen, and potassium hydroxide, calcium hydroxide and zinc oxide for the reactions with water. Write word equations for all these reactions.

5 Copper is sometimes used to cover the roofs of buildings and for the outer skin of statues (for example, the Statue of Liberty in New York Harbour). With time, the copper turns a green colour. In industrial areas, this green colour is usually due to a mixture of copper sulphate and copper hydroxide. In other areas, it is usually a mixture of copper carbonate and copper hydroxide.

a Explain why copper sulphate is formed in industrial areas but not elsewhere.
b Where does the carbon come from to form copper carbonate?
c Suggest word equations to describe the formation of the green colour on the roofs of buildings covered with copper.

6 Displacement reactions

1 Copy and complete the following sentences. Use the words below to fill the gaps. Each word may be used more than once.

zinc   displacement   reactivity   copper

When a more reactive metal is dipped in a solution containing a less reactive metal, a .... reaction takes place.

An example of this type of reaction is when a piece of .... is dipped in .... sulphate solution, when the .... metal displaces the .... from solution. Studying these reactions enables us to draw up a .... series.

2 Aluminium reacts with iron oxide in a reaction called the thermite reaction. In this reaction, the aluminium displaces the iron. The reaction releases a great deal of heat energy, leaving the iron liquid.

a Write a word equation for this reaction.
b The reaction is used to weld the ends of rails together when a railway track is laid. What makes it suitable for this purpose?

3 Iron will displace copper from a solution of copper sulphate, and magnesium will displace iron from a solution of iron sulphate.

a Write word equations for these reactions.
b Write down a reactivity series for these three metals, putting the most reactive metal first.

4 Some Martian school pupils carried out displacement reactions for the metals scrittiby, splerbity, snibitty, stobbity, slibbity and blib and their snerbide solutions. They collected the results shown in the table (at the bottom of the page), although they did not finish their investigation. If displacement took place they showed it by a ✓, if it did not, they put a ✗.

a Copy and complete the table as far as you can.
b As far as you can, draw up a reactivity series for the metals.
c What further investigation(s) would you need to do to produce a complete reactivity series?

5 The chemical formulae for magnesium sulphate, copper sulphate and zinc sulphate are $MgSO_4$, $CuSO_4$ and $ZnSO_4$, respectively. Write balanced chemical equations for the displacement reactions between magnesium, zinc and copper as metals and as sulphates in solution. Use the state symbols (aq) to indicate a solution ($MgSO_4$(aq) for example) and (s) to indicate a solid (Zn(s) for example).

Table for **Q4**

Metal	Scrittiby snerbide	Splerbity snerbide	Snibitty snerbide	Stobbity snerbide	Slibbity snerbide	Blib snerbide
Scrittiby	–	✗				✓
Splerbity		–	✓			
Snibitty			–		✓	
Stobbity	✓	✓	✓	–	✓	✓
Slibbity	✗	✗			–	
Blib		✗	✗		✓	–

1 Copy and complete the following sentences. Use the words below to fill the gaps.

**carbon   ore   concentrating   Earth
reducing   hydrogen**

Metals or metal compounds are usually found in the crust of the .... mixed with other substances. If there is enough metal/metal compound in a rock to be worth extracting, then the rock is called an ....

Extracting a metal from its ore usually involves three steps: .... , smelting or roasting, and then .... The last stage can be done in several ways – two substances that can be used are .... and ....

2 Old-time gold prospectors used panning to separate gold from surrounding material. In some adventure parks you can still pan for 'gold'. Use words and diagrams to explain how panning works.

3 Froth flotation can be used to separate a valuable mineral from worthless material in an ore. Explain how froth flotation works.

4 The production of lead from its ore, galena, involves roasting.

a What is roasting?
b If the formula of galena is PbS and the formula of lead oxide is PbO, write a word equation for the roasting of galena.

5 Zinc can be found in the Earth's crust combined with sulphur. To produce the pure metal, this sulphide must undergo a two-stage process. The first of these stages is roasting, while the second is reduction.

a Write a word equation to describe what happens when zinc sulphide is roasted.
b In the second stage of the process, two possible substances could be used – hydrogen and carbon.
  i Look at the reactivity series (see below) and decide whether you should use hydrogen or carbon to produce zinc.
  ii Explain your answer using a word equation.

Reactivity series of selected elements

potassium	most reactive
sodium	
calcium	
magnesium	
aluminium	
carbon	
zinc	
iron	
lead	
hydrogen	
copper	
silver	
gold	
platinum	least reactive

1 Rearrange these sentences to describe the production of iron from iron ore. Copy the sentences out in the correct order.

- Molten iron runs to the bottom of the blast furnace, where it can be tapped off.
- Iron ore is a type of iron oxide.
- Carbon monoxide reduces the iron oxide to iron.
- The slag runs to the bottom of the furnace, where it floats on top of the molten iron.
- In the blast furnace, coke burns in a stream of hot air, and produces a gas called carbon dioxide.
- Carbon dioxide reacts with more carbon to form another gas, called carbon monoxide.
- The limestone reacts with acidic impurities to form a molten slag.
- Coke and iron ore are mixed together and fed into a blast furnace, together with limestone.
- The reducing agent which is used to remove oxygen from iron oxide is carbon, in the form of coke.

2 Copy the diagram of the blast furnace. Use the labels below on your diagram.

- 1500 °C
- hot gases out
- blast of hot air in
- molten iron out
- mixture of iron ore, coke and limestone in
- molten slag out

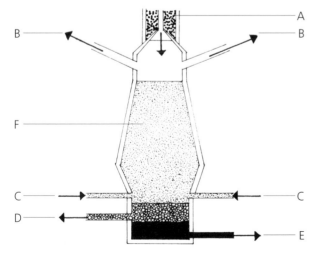

3 Write balanced chemical equations for the following reactions which occur in the blast furnace.

a Carbon and oxygen react to form carbon dioxide.
b Carbon dioxide reacts with carbon to form carbon monoxide.
c Iron ore (iron oxide) reacts with carbon monoxide to form iron and carbon dioxide.
d Limestone (calcium carbonate) decomposes to form calcium oxide and carbon dioxide.
e Calcium oxide reacts with impurities such as silica to form slag (calcium silicate).

Chemical formulae you may need:
- carbon dioxide, CO_2
- calcium carbonate, $CaCO_3$
- calcium silicate, $CaSiO_3$
- carbon, C
- silica, SiO_2
- carbon monoxide, CO
- calcium oxide, CaO
- iron oxide, Fe_2O_3
- oxygen, O_2

1 Copy and complete the following sentences. Use the words below to fill the gaps.

**electrolysis   current   electrolytes
conductors**

Electrical energy is carried by an electric
.... Metals are good .... of
electricity.

Electricity can also flow through solutions
called .... Unlike metals, these are
chemically changed when they conduct
electricity. This process is called ....

2 a Copy the diagram that shows a solution
being electrolysed. Use the labels below on
your diagram.

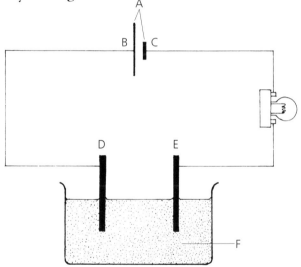

- +
- –
- battery
- anode (positive)
- cathode (negative)
- solution
b If this solution was water (H_2O), what would
be produced
  i at the anode
  ii at the cathode?

3 Match the name of the atom with the
symbol for its ion. Copy out the name and
symbol together.

O^{2-}	zinc	Cl^-	Pb^{2+}
copper	Br^-	bromine	Cu^{2+}
calcium	H^+	lead	chlorine
Zn^{2+}	oxygen	hydrogen	Ca^{2+}

4 Copy and complete the table to show what
is formed when some solutions are electrolysed.

Solution	Cathode	Anode
copper chloride		
zinc bromide		
hydrochloric acid		

5 Copper can be purified by electrolytic
refining, in which copper is removed from an
impure anode and is deposited on a pure
copper cathode. The half-equation for the
reaction at the anode is
$$Cu(s) \longrightarrow Cu^{2+}(aq) + 2e^-$$

a Write down the half-equation for the reaction
at the cathode.
b How do the electrons get from the anode to
the cathode?
c One mole of electrons travels from the anode
to the cathode. What mass of copper is
deposited on the cathode? (The relative
atomic mass of copper is 64.)

1 Rearrange these sentences to describe the production of aluminium from bauxite. Copy the sentences out in the correct order.

- Aluminium metal is formed at the cathode.
- Aluminium is extracted by electrolysis, since it is above carbon in the reactivity series.
- A current passes through carbon electrodes into the molten mixture.
- Aluminium is found in the ore bauxite.
- Oxygen forms at the other electrode, reacting with it to form carbon dioxide.
- To extract aluminium, the ore is dissolved in another, less common, ore of aluminium, called cryolite, which is heated to almost 1000 °C.

2 **a** In the production of aluminium from its ore, why is it not possible to use silver electrodes?
b What metals could possibly be used to make the electrodes? (Use the data sheet, page 169.)

3 Use the reactivity series of metals (see page 169) to answer these questions, explaining the reasons for your answers carefully.

a Which metals must be extracted from their ores using electrolysis?
b Which metals are found naturally in the Earth's crust, uncombined with other elements?

4 There is more aluminium in the Earth's crust than any other metal. What are the arguments in favour of recycling aluminium?

5 The diagram shows the electrolysis of bauxite (aluminium oxide).

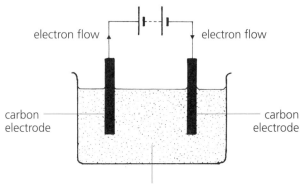

electron flow   electron flow

carbon electrode   carbon electrode

molten aluminium oxide/cryolite mixture

a Write down half-equations for the processes occurring at
  i the anode
  ii the cathode.
b Copy the diagram and add suitable details to it to show the processes occurring at each electrode.
c Copy and complete these two statements.
  i Oxidation (................ of electrons) occurs at the ....
  ii Reduction (............ of electrons) occurs at the ....

1 Copy and complete the following sentences, choosing the correct ending in each case.

a Substances which change colour according to whether they are in acid, neutral or alkaline solutions are called.....

b When a substance dissolves in water it forms a solution which may be.....

c The pH scale is.....

d When non-metal oxides dissolve in water.....

e When metal oxides dissolve in water.....

Choose the endings from:
- .....acidic, neutral or alkaline.
- .....their solutions are acidic, with a pH less than 7.
- .....indicators.
- .....their solutions are alkaline, with a pH greater than 7.
- .....used to show how acidic or alkaline a solution is.

2 Choose the symbol which is used to indicate that a substance is corrosive to living tissues.

Copy the symbol and label your drawing 'The symbol used to show that a substance attacks and destroys living tissues, including eyes and skin. A substance like this is called corrosive.'

3 Copy out the scale representing the pH scale.

```
   1     3     5     7     9     11    13
   |--+--|--+--|--+--|--+--|--+--|--+--|
```

Indicate on the scale the approximate pH of
a vinegar (a weak acid)
b pure water
c caustic soda (a strong alkali)
d hydrochloric acid (a strong acid)
e toothpaste (a weak alkali).

4 Not all indicators change colour at the same pH. The table shows the names of some indicators. It also shows the colour change which occurs as the pH increases (the solution becomes more alkaline) and the approximate pH at which this happens.

Indicator	Colour change as pH increases	Approximate pH at which change occurs
methyl orange	red ⟶ orange	4
litmus	red ⟶ blue	5
bromothymol blue	yellow ⟶ blue	7
phenolphthalein	colourless ⟶ pink	9

a Make another copy of the scale in **Q3**. Add labelled arrows to the scale to show where the indicators change colour.

b Which indicator could be used to distinguish a solution which is weakly acidic from a solution which is strongly acidic?

c Which indicator could be used to distinguish a solution which is weakly alkaline from a solution which is strongly alkaline?

d Which indicator could be used to distinguish a solution which is weakly alkaline from a solution which is weakly acidic?

12 *Metals and acids*

1 Copy and complete the following sentences. Use the words below to fill the gaps.

**hydrogen   smaller   bubbles of gas
reactive   reacts**

When a metal reacts with an acid .... are seen – these are .... As a piece of metal reacts, it gets .... as it .... with the acid. The more .... the metal, the faster it reacts.

2 When metals react with an acid, a gas is given off. Describe carefully the tests you would do on a test tube of this gas to show what it is.

3 Three metals A, B and C were each put into some strong acid. The amount of gas produced by each metal was measured, and graphs were plotted.

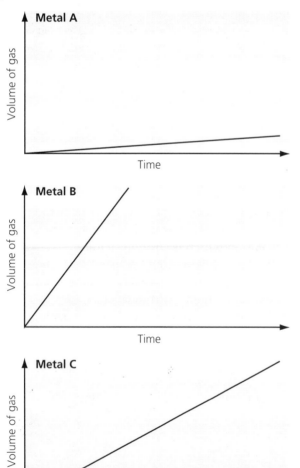

a Which metal produced hydrogen quickest?
b Which metal produced hydrogen slowest?
c Put the three metals in order of reactivity, with the most reactive first.
d How would you make sure that this investigation was a fair test?

4 Using words and diagrams, describe how you would investigate the reaction of the metals copper, magnesium and zinc with hydrochloric acid (a strong acid). You can use the equipment shown below.

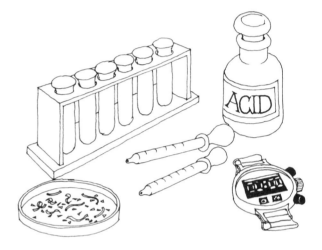

5 Using words and diagrams, describe how you would investigate the reaction of iron, calcium and the three metals from **Q4** with hydrochloric acid (a strong acid) and ethanoic acid (a weak acid). Use the equipment shown in **Q4**. Think carefully about how you will make this a fair test.

1 Copy and complete the following sentences. Use the words below to fill the gaps.

metal   salt   indigestion   neutralisation

When acids and bases react, the reaction is called .... This can be summarised as

acid + base ⟶ .... + water.

Bases are often .... compounds such as oxides, hydroxides, hydrogen carbonates and carbonates. Bases such as magnesium hydroxide are used in medicines to cure ....

2 'Bicarbonate for bees, vinegar for vasps (wasps!)' is one saying used to remember how to treat bee and wasp stings. What does this tell you about the pH of bee and wasp stings?

3 Chalk (calcium carbonate) is sometimes dumped into lakes affected by acid rain.

a Burning fossil fuels produces sulphur dioxide. Why can this lead to acid rain?
b Why can it be helpful to add chalk to lakes affected by acid rain?
c Why not use sodium hydroxide instead of chalk?

4 Write word equations to describe the products of the following reactions:

a zinc oxide + hydrochloric acid
b magnesium oxide + sulphuric acid
c copper carbonate + nitric acid
d sodium carbonate + ethanoic acid

5 Describe carefully how you would produce a pure sample of copper sulphate crystals. You can use the equipment shown below.

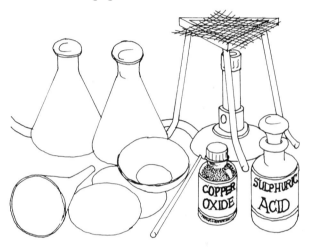

14 A model for neutralisation

1 Copy and complete the following sentences, choosing the correct ending in each case.

a All acids are.....

b When an acid is dissolved in water it forms.....

c When an alkali dissolves in water it forms.....

d When an acidic solution reacts with an alkaline solution.....

e An acid reacting with an alkali is called.....

Choose the endings from:

- .....hydrogen ions, H^+.
- .....hydroxide ions, OH^-.
- .....substances which contain hydrogen.
- .....a neutralisation reaction.
- .....H^+ and OH^- ions combine to form water.

2 Acid salts are salts which contain some hydrogen ions. One example of an acid salt is sodium hydrogen sulphate, $NaHSO_4$, a white powder found in some lavatory cleaners. Sodium hydrogen sulphate is especially good for cleaning lavatories and basins in hard water areas, where limescale (calcium and magnesium carbonates) builds up.

a Explain why sodium hydrogen sulphate is useful in hard water areas.

b Write an equation to explain what happens when sodium hydrogen sulphate is poured onto limescale. Hint: Treat sodium hydrogen sulphate as a mixture of sodium sulphate (which is not involved in the reaction) and sulphuric acid.

c Why is water needed before sodium hydrogen sulphate can act as a cleaner in this situation?

3 When an acidic solution and an alkaline solution neutralise each other, a good deal of energy is released.

a What effect does this energy have on the two solutions being mixed?

b Design a simple experiment to demonstrate to some younger pupils that neutralisation reactions are exothermic (release energy). Use words and diagrams to explain your ideas.

4 The diagram shows three pairs of beakers. Copy each pair of beakers, and then draw a third beaker in which the contents of the first two beakers are mixed. Draw lines between the ions that react.

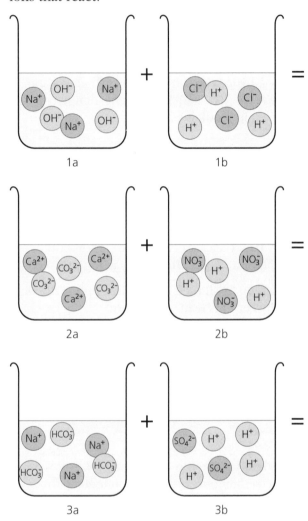

5 Write ionic equations for the reactions in **Q4**.

1 Copy and complete the following sentences. Use the words below to fill the gaps.

pieces cemented rain sediment rivers

Rocks on the surface of the Earth are attacked by wind, ... and frost. They are broken up into .... These then get washed into .... and rolled down to the sea. This .... settles out into layers. These are squashed and the pieces are .... together to make a new, hard, sedimentary rock. The rocks have been recycled!

2 Grit, pebbles, silt and sand are pieces of broken rock of different sizes.

a Arrange them in order of increasing size.
b Copy out the table, putting the correct names in place of the letters A–D.

Size of broken rock (mm)	Name
0.004 to 0.06	A
0.06 to 2	B
2 to 4	C
4 to 64	D

c What would you call a piece of rock 1 mm across?
d What would you call a piece of rock 10 mm across?

3 Look at the three diagrams that show how loose sediment turns into sedimentary rock. Copy them, adding the correct caption from those given below.

A The water contains dissolved salts that sometimes crystallise out.
B Sand grains have gaps between them, which fill with water.
C The crystals cement the sand grains together, making a hard rock.

4 Use this key to identify the sedimentary rocks described below. Write a brief description of each rock type, using your answers to the key questions.

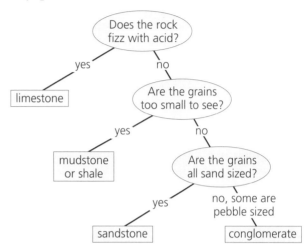

Rock A does not fizz with acid. It is made of a fine grey material and shows a layered structure. There are some fossil sea shells in it, but the individual grains are too small to see.

Rock B does not fizz with acid. It is made of large, well-rounded pebbles up to 5 cm across, set in a finer-grained matrix.

Rock C is made up almost entirely of broken sea shells. Their broken surfaces sparkle in the light. It fizzes with acid.

Rock D does not fizz with acid. It is a uniform yellowbrown colour and is fairly hard, but if you rub it you can make parts of it crumble into fine sand grains. There are no fossils.

5 Look at these diagrams of large rock fragments.

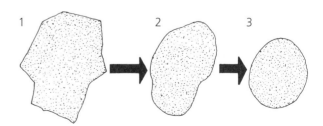

a Which rock was found in the mountains?
b Which rock was found on a beach?
c Which rock was found in a fast river?
d Explain why their shapes are different.

71

2 The igneous rocks

1 Copy and complete the following sentences. Use the words below to fill the gaps.

magma igneous random crystals

All .... rocks are formed from molten rock which is called .... As the liquid rock cools and sets, ... form which lock together to make a hard rock. The crystals grow at .... , so the rock they form does not show any bands.

2 Look carefully at the words and definitions. Match each word to its definition and then copy them out.

Magma   a light-coloured rock containing large, interlocking crystals.

Lava   the type of igneous rock that forms on the surface of the Earth; an example is basalt.

Volcano   the central hollow at the top of a volcano.

Crater   a dark, hard, extrusive igneous rock.

Extrusive   a cone-shaped structure built on the surface of the Earth by lava and ash.

Intrusive   the type of igneous rock that cools and sets deep within the Earth; an example is granite.

Granite   any form of molten rock.

Basalt   molten rock that pours out onto the surface of the Earth.

3 Parts of Hadrian's Wall in Northumberland are built on an outcrop of a hard igneous rock, called an igneous intrusion. This rock formed when magma was squeezed into a crack between some beds of sedimentary rock. At the edges of the outcrop, the crystals are too small to see – the rock is just like basalt. In the middle of the outcrop, however, they are much larger, up to 1 mm across.

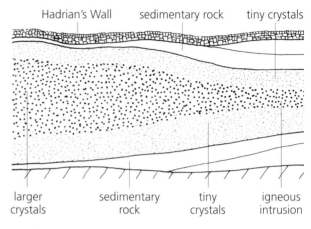

larger crystals   sedimentary rock   tiny crystals   igneous intrusion

a Why does basalt usually have tiny crystals?

b Why does granite have large crystals?

c Use these ideas to explain the change in crystal size across the minor intrusion shown.

4 Mount Vesuvius in southern Italy is a volcano that 'seals itself up' between eruptions, because lava sets in the crater. Gas pressure builds up underneath until it is great enough to 'blow' the lava plug, like a champagne cork popping when the bottle is shaken. Look at the figures below.

Year of eruption	Years since last eruption	Millions of cubic metres of lava
1944	15	25
1929	23	12
1906	34	80
1872	14	20
1858	64	120
1794	34	27

a Plot a graph of the amount of lava against the time between the eruptions.

b Is there a correlation? If so, how strong is it?

c Draw a line of best fit.

d Use the line of best fit to predict the volume of lava that might be produced if Vesuvius erupted today.

e Lava from the 1944 eruption reached the outskirts of Naples. Should people living in Naples be worried at the moment? Explain your answer.

1 Copy and complete the following sentences, which describe the rock cycle. Use the words below to fill the gaps.

metamorphic weathered igneous sedimentary magma transported

a Igneous rocks are .... and eroded on the surface of the Earth.
b The pieces are .... to the sea where they form beds of sediment.
c Over time, the sediment is compressed and turns to .... rock.
d If the rock is buried, heated and squeezed, it can change to form .... rock.
e If metamorphic rock is heated further, it can melt to form ....
f Magma then cools and sets to form .... rock, and the cycle continues.

2 Copy and complete the following sentences. Use the words below to fill the gaps.

metamorphic igneous

a .... rock is made from tightly interlocking crystals arranged randomly.
b .... rock is made from tightly interlocking crystals arranged in bands.

3 Copy this diagram of the rock cycle. Use the labels at the top of the next column in place of the letters A–H on your diagram.

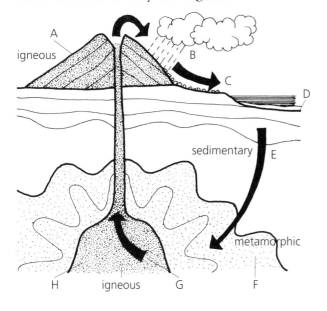

- If magma cools underground it forms large crystals.
- Rivers transport the sediment to the sea.
- If metamorphic rock is heated further it melts to form magma.
- Ice, wind and rain break up rocks.
- Sediments harden to form sedimentary rock.
- Magma cools rapidly on the surface – small crystals form.
- If sediments are deeply buried, heat and pressure may change them to metamorphic rock.
- Beds of sediment form in the sea.

4 Use this key to decide whether the following rocks are igneous, sedimentary or metamorphic. Write out your answers with reasons for your identification.

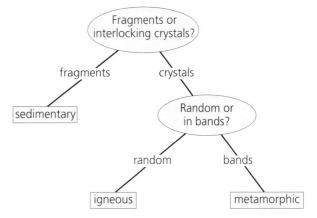

A Gneiss is a hard, crystalline rock. The crystals are arranged in coarse bands.
B Breccia is made from angular, broken rock fragments that have been cemented together.
C Andesite is a dark, often purple-coloured rock. Under the microscope you can see that it is made up of a random mass of tightly interlocking crystals.
D Gabbro is a black/white speckled rock, made up of a jumbled, higgledy-piggledy mass of tightly interlocking black ferromagnesian and white felspar crystals.
E Phyllite is a smooth, shiny, greenish rock, made of tiny, platy crystals arranged in layers.

4 Finding out about the past

1 Copy and complete the following sentences. Use the words below to fill the gaps.

fossil   old   sediment

The remains of living creatures sometimes get buried in _____ . If this hardens to form sedimentary rock, the remains can be preserved as a _____ . Older rocks show different types of fossils than younger rocks. Fossils can help to tell how _____ a layer of rock is.

2 Fossils can tell you about the environment where the rocks formed. Look at the diagram below.

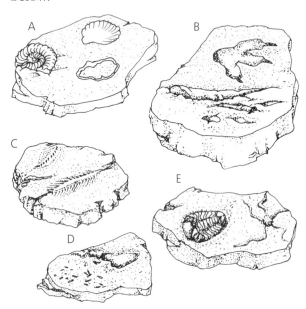

Do you think the following sedimentary rocks formed on land or in the sea? Give a reason for your answer.

Rock A is grey shale containing fossils of cockle and oyster shells, as well as coiled ammonites.

Rock B is siltstone that shows fossil tree branches and leaves. There is an impression of a dinosaur footprint.

Rock C is limestone containing fossil corals.

Rock D is made of silty mudstone. It contains grass seeds and the foot and hoof of a primitive horse.

Rock E is made of silty mudstone. It shows the fossils of a starfish and a trilobite.

3 The diagram below shows the time eras in which different types of fossils have been found.

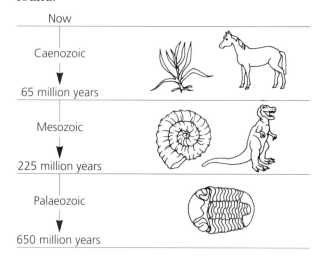

a Which era did rock A from **Q2** form in? How do you know?
b What is the possible age of rock A? Give the range of ages possible (in millions of years).
c Why are ammonites not found in Caenozoic rock?
d Why are ammonites not found in Palaeozoic rocks?

4 The Grand Canyon in Arizona, USA, cuts through horizontal layers of sedimentary rock.

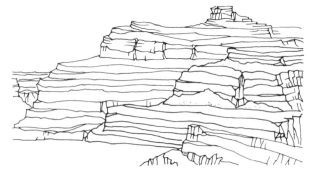

a Where will you find the oldest rocks, at the top or at the bottom? Explain your answer.

Look back at **Q2** and **Q3** to answer part **b**.
b Some rocks are siltstones from the oldest part of the Mesozoic era. Which rock described in **Q2** could have come from there? Explain your answer.

1 Copy and complete the following sentences. Use the words below to fill the gaps.

quicklime chippings cement rock calcium

Limestone is a common sedimentary ....
It is used for building stone and road ....
It is mostly made of .... carbonate. If this is heated in a kiln, it changes into ....
This can be used to improve the soil. It is also used to make ....

2 **a** When calcium carbonate is heated, it breaks down to give calcium oxide and the gas carbon dioxide.
Complete this word equation:

.... $\longrightarrow$ .... + ...
(limestone) heat (quicklime)

b Quicklime reacts with water to make slaked lime (calcium hydroxide).
Complete this word equation:

.... + ... $\longrightarrow$ ....
(quicklime) (slaked lime)

3 Copy this diagram and use it to answer the questions.

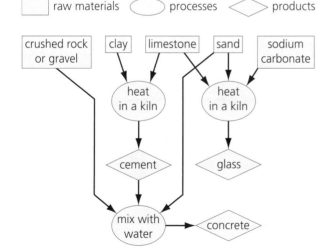

☐ raw materials ⬭ processes ◇ products

a Describe how cement is made.
b Describe how concrete is made.
c Describe how glass is made.

4 The percentage by weight of the four components of concrete, A–D, is as follows:

A 6% **B** 12% **C** 34% **D** 48%

Jack the builder says he makes concrete by mixing 4 shovel-fulls of gravel, 3 of sand and 1 of cement with a little water. Match this recipe to the information above, and list the percentage of gravel, sand, cement and water in a good concrete mix.

5 Read this passage about concrete and cement.

On the face of it, concrete seems an environmentally friendly building material. The raw materials are common and harmless, and concrete itself is unreactive and certainly non-toxic. The problem is that the cement used in concrete production is produced by heating clay and limestone to very high temperatures in kilns – so its production is very energy intensive. In the USA, cement production was found to be ten times as energy intensive as industrial processes in general. In some developing countries, cement production accounts for up to two-thirds of the energy they use.

As coal is often used to fuel the kilns, cement production also results in the production of vast amounts of carbon dioxide. This is added to the carbon dioxide that is produced during the chemical reaction when the limestone is heated. Combined, they add up to well over a tonne of carbon dioxide for every tonne of cement produced. Carbon dioxide is the main greenhouse gas that is causing global warming.

a Why does concrete seem to be a good material at first?
b What are the two 'hidden' environmental costs?
c A new cement kiln is to be set up near you. The firm has put out a lot of positive publicity about the benefits of 'harmless' cement and concrete. Write a letter to your local paper, giving the counter-arguments against cement production.

6 Fossil fuels

1 Rearrange these sentences to describe how oil was formed. Copy the sentences out in the correct order.

- They broke down, forming drops of oil and bubbles of gas.
- They were sealed up, away from oxygen.
- The remains were heated and squeezed over millions of years.
- The sediment was buried deeper and deeper.
- The remains of living things became trapped in sediment.

2 This diagram shows how wood can be made to produce products similar to the three fossil fuels (coal, oil and gas) in the laboratory.

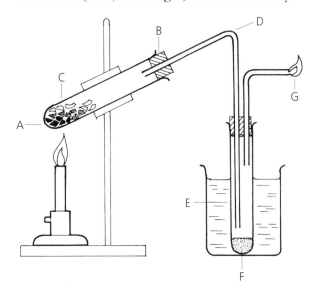

Copy the diagram in the centre of a page. Use the labels below in place of the letters A–G on your diagram.

- Wood is heated in a closed tube.
- Gases boil off.
- **Oil** (and water) collect in the tube.
- The cold water cools and condenses some of the gas.
- **Charcoal** is left behind – this is like **coal**.
- **Gas** comes out here – you can burn it!
- No oxygen can get in, so the wood doesn't burn.

3 If you mix 50 ml of water with 50 ml of oil, the new volume is 100 ml. If you mix 50 ml of water with 50 ml of sand, however, the new volume may only be 85 ml.

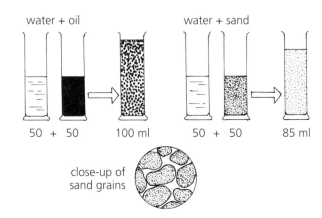

water + oil   water + sand

50 + 50   100 ml   50 + 50   85 ml

close-up of sand grains

a Where has the 'missing' water gone? (Clue: look at the close-up of sand grains.)
b Use this idea to explain how oil is trapped in the sandstone rocks beneath the North Sea.

4 When you wash up a greasy plate, the oil floats up to the surface as it is less dense than the water. Bubbles rise up and float, too! Rocks beneath the sea are 'full up' with water. Even on land, deeply buried rocks are 'full' of groundwater.

a Use these ideas to explain how oil and gas gradually rise upwards from deeply buried sediment. Clay is non-porous. Oil and gas cannot pass through it.
b Explain how a dome-shaped bed of clay can trap oil and gas beneath it. Why would it not work if the bed was straight and simply tilted?
c Copy the diagram below.

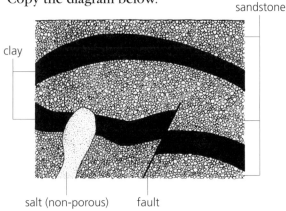

sandstone

clay

salt (non-porous)   fault

Mark in three places where you might expect to find oil and gas collecting. (Clue: anywhere that the oil is stopped from rising by a layer of clay.)
Draw on three oil wells that would strike it rich.

1 Copy and complete the following sentences. Use the words below to fill the gaps.

atoms   hydrocarbons   molecules

Crude oil is a mixture of compounds called
.... These contain particles called
.... , made from carbon and hydrogen
.... joined together in chains.

2 Copy this diagram, which shows the apparatus used to separate crude oil into its fractions in the laboratory. Use the labels below in place of the letters A–E on your diagram.

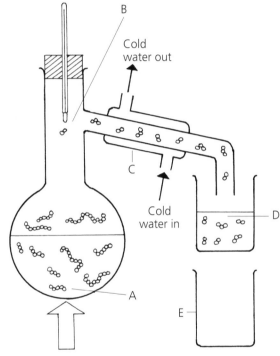

- The lighter, smaller particles boil off first, at a low temperature.
- Cold water cools the gas particles and makes them condense.
- Crude oil is heated in the flask.
- The beaker is changed as the temperature rises, to collect different fractions.
- The liquid collects in the beaker.

3 Copy the diagram (at the top of the next column) of a fractionating column. Use the labels below the diagram in place of the letters A–D on your diagram.

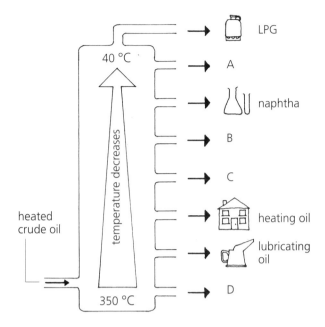

- **Petrol** is used as fuel for cars (bp 40–100 °C)
- **Bitumen** is used to make roads (bp over 400 °C)
- **Diesel** is used as lorry fuel (bp 220–300 °C)
- **Paraffin** (kerosene) is used for jet fuel (bp 150–240 °C)

4 Here is some information about the boiling points of some hydrocarbons.

Number of carbon atoms	Boiling point (°C)
5	36
6	69
7	99
9	151
10	174

a Plot a graph of boiling point against number of carbon atoms.
b What happens to the boiling point as the number of carbon atoms goes up?
c Use your graph to predict the boiling point of octane – a hydrocarbon with eight carbon atoms in its chain. Octane is found in petrol.
d In a laboratory experiment, Sasha collected 3 fractions from a sample of crude oil. They boiled at:
   A 50–90 °C   **B** 100–140 °C   **C** 150–200 °C
Which of these could be used as petrol? Explain your answer.

1 Copy and complete the following sentences. Use the words below to fill the gaps.

cracking   plastics   temperatures hydrocarbon

The fractional distillation of crude oil produces more large .... molecules than are needed. Fortunately, these can be 'chopped up' into smaller molecules by a process called .... This happens when the hydrocarbons are heated to very high .... Cracking makes more petrol, but it also makes special molecules that are used to make

....

2 Draw a pie chart to show the relative proportions of different products that may be obtained from crude oil if 100 000 tonnes makes:

- 30 000 tonnes petrol
- 7 000 tonnes naphtha
- 10 000 tonnes kerosene
- 30 000 tonnes diesel
- 20 000 tonnes fuel oil
- 3 000 tonnes others

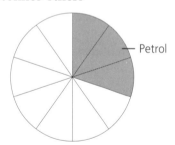

— Petrol

3 Copy and complete the following sentences. Choose the correct word from each of the pairs given.

Crude oil hydrocarbons are called **alkanes / alkenes**. Their carbon atoms are joined by **single / double** bonds. They cannot form any extra bonds so they are said to be **saturated / unsaturated**. When hydrocarbons are cracked, **alkanes / alkenes** such as ethene are formed. Ethene has a **single / double** bond. This can open up to add more atoms, so ethene is said to be **saturated / unsaturated**.

4 **a** Draw a diagram of the simple alkane, **hexane**, which has six carbon atoms (C_6H_{14}).

b Hexane can be cracked to give the alkene **ethene** (C_2H_4) as well as an alkane **A**. Draw a diagram of ethene.

c How many carbon atoms must there be in alkane **A**? How many hydrogen atoms?

d Draw a diagram of alkane **A**.

5 **a** Use these diagrams to help you explain how ethene may be polymerised to make polythene.

ethene monomer

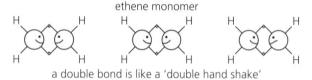

a double bond is like a 'double hand shake'

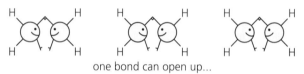

one bond can open up...

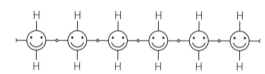

and the monomers can link up in an addition polymer

polymerisation

the double bond opens

...to give a repeating unit with a free 'arm' at each end

b Propene is an alkene with three carbon atoms. It is like ethene, with an extra CH_3 in place of one of the hydrogen atoms. It can be drawn like this:

or

Draw diagrams like those for ethene, to show how propene could undergo addition polymerisation to form polypropene.

1 Copy and complete the following sentences. Use the words below to fill the gaps.

oxides oxygen reacting combustion nitrogen

The air is roughly four-fifths .... and one-fifth .... When things burn in air, they are .... with the oxygen. New compounds called .... are formed, and energy is given out. The scientific word for burning is

....

2 When carbon burns in air it forms the colourless gas, carbon dioxide.

a Copy and complete the word equation for this reaction:

carbon + ... ⟶ ....

b When carbon burns, it seems to disappear. Where does it go?

3 When hydrogen burns, it forms hydrogen oxide vapour.

a What is the common name we give to this new chemical? (Hint: it's usually a liquid when you see it.)

b Copy and complete the word equation for this reaction.

hydrogen + ... ⟶ ....

4 Fuels are chemicals which we burn to get energy.

a Copy and complete the generalised word equation for this reaction.

fuel + ... ⟶ waste gases + energy

b What type of chemicals will these waste gases be? (Check back to **Q1**.)

5 Many fuels, such as oil and gas, are chemicals that contain both carbon and hydrogen.

a What two oxides would you expect to find in the waste gases when this type of fuel burns?

b Copy and complete the word equation:

fuel + ... ⟶ .... + ...
                                            + energy

6 This apparatus is used to identify the waste gases produced when a candle burns.

a Copy the diagram. Use the labels below in place of the letters A–F in your diagram.

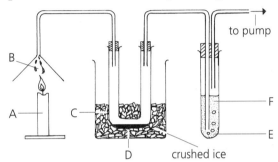

- The crushed ice cools the gases.
- The limewater turns milky.
- Candle wax contains carbon and hydrogen.
- The gas bubbles through limewater.
- The waste gases rise into the funnel.
- A colourless liquid condenses and collects.

b The colourless liquid turns white anhydrous copper sulphate powder blue. What is this liquid? Add a label to your diagram.

c What is the gas that turns limewater milky? Add a label to your diagram.

7 Is it possible to weld or cut metal under water? Special blowtorches can. They mix gases from two separate cylinders. The two gases then burn together, even under water. One of the gases is a fuel. What must the other gas be? Explain your answer.

8 **a** If you heat potassium nitrate it melts and then bubbles as a gas is given off. The gas relights a glowing splint. What do you think the gas might be?

b Gunpowder contains carbon and sulphur, mixed with potassium nitrate. Gunpowder will burn, even if there is no air. Explain why this is possible.

c What two waste gases do you think will be formed when gunpowder burns? Explain your answer.

10 Polluting the air

1 Copy and complete the following sentences. Use the words below to fill the gaps.

acidic dioxide rain fish sulphuric sulphur

Many fuels contain .... as an impurity. When this burns it produces sulphur .... gas. This gas dissolves in the .... and reacts with the air to form weak .... acid. This makes the rain .... Acid rain can damage buildings and kill .... and plants.

2 Most fuels contain a percentage of sulphur.

Fuel type	% Sulphur
jet fuel	0.05
gasoline (petrol)	0.03
kerosene (paraffin)	0.09
diesel fuel	0.18
light fuel oil	0.24
heavy fuel oil	2.01

a Which fuel is likely to produce the least sulphur dioxide gas per tonne when it is burnt?

b Which fuel is likely to produce the most sulphur dioxide gas per tonne when it is burnt?

c Heavy fuel oil is burnt in oil-fired power stations. Why is it so important that they treat their waste gases to remove pollutants before releasing them into the air?

d Plot a bar chart of the % of sulphur in the different fuels, leaving out heavy fuel oil.

3 Cars burn their fuel inside the engine. The fuel explodes and drives the pistons. Under these conditions small amounts of new pollutant gases form: nitrogen oxides (which are acidic gases) and carbon monoxide.

a Carbon monoxide is a poisonous gas. Why shouldn't you run a car engine inside a closed garage?

b Where does the nitrogen come from that forms the nitrogen oxides? (Clue: where do cars get the oxygen from to react with the fuel?)

4 These pie charts show the sources of three pollutant gases in the atmosphere (of Canada).

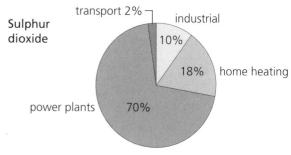

Sulphur dioxide: transport 2%, industrial 10%, home heating 18%, power plants 70%

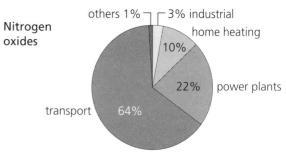

Nitrogen oxides: others 1%, 3% industrial, home heating 10%, power plants 22%, transport 64%

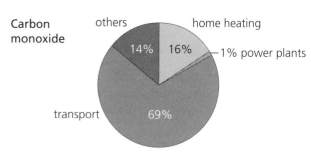

Carbon monoxide: others 14%, home heating 16%, 1% power plants, transport 69%

a What is the largest source of sulphur dioxide?

b What are the major pollutants produced by the transport industry?

c Nitrogen oxides and carbon monoxide combine to produce photochemical smog. Why do you think this type of smog is most common in the cities?

5 Carbon dioxide is produced when fossil fuels burn. This gas causes a greenhouse effect. Rearrange these sentences to explain the greenhouse effect. Copy the sentences out in the correct order.

• The Earth is warmed and gives off heat rays.
• Sunlight passes in through the atmosphere.
• Carbon dioxide in the atmosphere traps the heat rays, so the Earth warms up.

11 *The evolving atmosphere*

1 Copy the table showing the link between the evolution of life and the changing atmosphere on Earth.

Million years ago	Life and conditions on Earth	Atmosphere
4500	Molten Earth – no life	**A**
3000	First primitive life – single cells that get energy from the Sun	Carbon dioxide
2000	Simple blue-green algae are more common, producing oxygen as a waste gas during photosynthesis	**B**
1500	**C**	Oxygen starts to build up in the atmosphere – the ozone layer starts to form, protecting the Earth's surface
1000	Green algae evolve in this 'safer' environment – the first simple animals evolve	Oxygen reacts with ammonia to give some nitrogen
600	**D**	Carbon dioxide is lost from the atmosphere as it gets locked up in the calcium carbonate shells – limestone forms
300	Life evolves on land	More carbon dioxide lost as coal forms – bacteria release more nitrogen
200	Plant/animal balance more or less as today	**E**

a Use the phrases below in place of the letters A–E in your table.
- Atmosphere settles down to one-fifth oxygen and four-fifths nitrogen, as today.
- Blue-green algae spread.
- Mostly carbon dioxide, with some methane and ammonia.
- Burst of animal evolution – shellfish flourish in the shallow seas.
- Oxygen 'pollutes' the seas, but does not get into the atmosphere yet.

b Where did all the carbon dioxide from the original atmosphere go? (Two answers needed.)

c How did the nitrogen get into the atmosphere? (Give two reasons.)

d Why is the oxygen referred to as 'polluting' the seas? (Hint: what did the oxygen do to the organisms that had evolved earlier?)

2 Carbon dioxide is a greenhouse gas. The graph shows the amount of carbon dioxide in the atmosphere over the last 1000 years, as trapped in Antarctic ice.

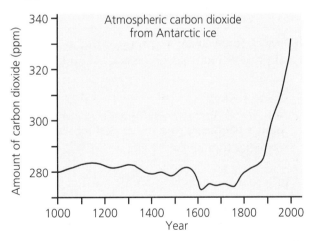

a Describe in words what this graph shows.

b What natural processes will put extra carbon dioxide into the atmosphere?

c Could a major volcanic eruption cause a pattern like this? If not, why not?

d What human activity over the last 200 years might have caused this increase?

e What do you think has happened to the average temperature of the Earth over the last 200 years?

1 Copy and complete the following sentences. Use the words below to fill the gaps.

iron evidence planet mantle crust mines

The Earth is a .... , a great ball of rock spinning through space. It has a diameter of 13 000 km, but our deepest .... go just 13 km into the surface.

We cannot see what is inside, but scientific .... tells us it is like a soft-boiled egg. A thin, hard .... covers a softer, rocky layer called the .... Deep inside is a core of molten ....

2 Look at this print out from a seismometer, showing an earthquake.

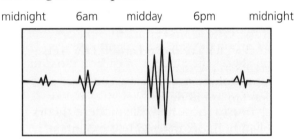

a When did the first shock wave appear?
b A second minor tremor occurred at 6am. Was it more or less powerful than the first? How do you know?
c When did the main earthquake occur? Explain your reasons.
d What happened at **i** 6pm? **ii** 9pm?

3 Rearrange these sentences to explain how meteorites help us to understand the Earth's composition. Copy the sentences out in the correct order.

- This suggests that the Earth is made from a rocky layer over an iron core.
- Meteorites are pieces of 'broken planet' that crash into the Earth.
- Overall, the density of the Earth is 5.5 g/cm^3, half way between rocks and iron.
- Some meteorites are made of iron (density 8 g/cm^3), others of rock (density 3 g/cm^3).
- The rocks of the Earth have a density like that of rocky meteorites.

4 Copy the diagram of the cross-section of the Earth. Use the labels below in place of the letters A–F on your diagram.

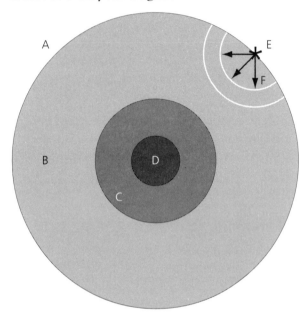

- The **outer core** is molten iron and nickel.
- The **crust** is thin – like a postage stamp on a football.
- The **inner core** is solid.
- The crust is cracked in places. Earthquakes occur when the cracked pieces move along faults.
- Earthquake shock waves pass down through the Earth – they help to give us an 'X-ray' picture.
- The **mantle** is semi-liquid, slow-moving rock.

5 The Earth has a magnetic field – that's why compasses point North. Do you think that this magnetic field comes from the mantle or the core? Explain your answer.

6 When the Earth first formed it was completely mixed up and molten.

a Which part cooled and solidified first?
b Why is the iron now found in the core of the Earth, with the rocky mantle above it?

13 Tecton the builder

1 Copy and complete the following sentences. Use the words below to fill the gaps.

erosion overturned mountains forces youngest

Sedimentary rocks form in horizontal layers with the .... at the top. But in places you can find them folded, faulted, tilted to high angles or even ....

This shows that the surface of the Earth is very unstable and that powerful .... are at work. These forces can slowly build up new .... , to replace those worn down by weathering and ....

2 The Earth is hot inside due to natural radioactivity. The heat energy is transferred through the mantle in the same way that heat is transferred through the water in a beaker over a Bunsen burner.

a Copy these two diagrams. Use the labels on the water beaker diagram to help you complete the labels on the section through the Earth.

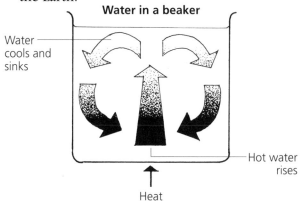

Water in a beaker

Water cools and sinks
Hot water rises
Heat

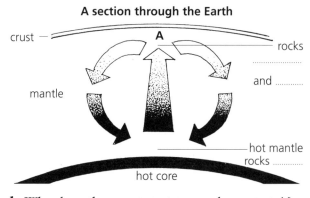

A section through the Earth

crust
mantle
A
rocks
and ....
hot mantle rocks ....
hot core

b Why does the crust start to crack apart at **A**?

3 In the past, people tried to explain the existence of oceans by saying that the Earth was getting bigger, so the crust had cracked.

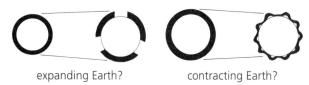

expanding Earth?   contracting Earth?

Other people tried to explain the existence of fold mountains by saying that the Earth had shrunk and the crust had wrinkled up.

a Copy the diagrams and write a few words to explain these old ideas.
b The Earth has both oceans *and* fold mountains. Why did these old ideas have to be replaced?

4 The modern theory of Plate Tectonics says that the crust is broken up into pieces called plates, which are moved around by convection currents in the mantle.

Copy these diagrams and write a sentence about each one to show how the modern theory can explain both oceans *and* fold mountains.

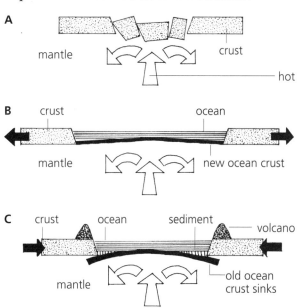

A
mantle   crust
hot

B
crust   ocean
mantle   new ocean crust

C
crust   ocean   sediment   volcano
mantle   old ocean crust sinks

D
new fold mountain
crust
mantle

1 **a** South America and Africa were once joined. Look at the diagram and list three pieces of evidence that show this.

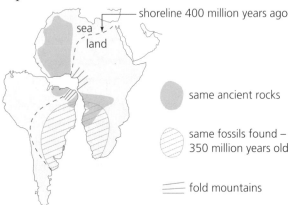

b In places, the Atlantic Ocean is 4000 km wide. Using lasers, it is possible to measure the distance so accurately that we know it is getting wider by about 2 cm every year.

Copy and complete this table and use it to work out how old the Atlantic Ocean is. (Note: this is just a rough approximation.)

Distance	Time taken
2 m	.... years
20 m	1000 years
20 km	1.......................... years
2000 km	.... years
4000 km	.... years

2 When new ocean crust forms, iron-rich minerals in the basaltic magma pick up the Earth's magnetic field. As the magnetic field reverses every half a million years or so, this produces a symmetrical pattern on either side of a spreading oceanic ridge.

Copy these diagrams and annotate them to explain how this works.

3 The Andes mountains formed when the old oceanic crust in the Pacific Ocean started to sink beneath the lighter South American continental plate.

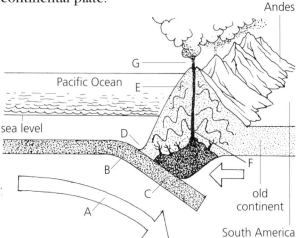

a Copy this diagram. Use the labels below in place of the letters A–G on your diagram.
  • Sediments squeezed up into folds.
  • Old, cold oceanic crust sinks back into the mantle.
  • Powerful earthquakes occur along the subduction zone.
  • Explosive volcanoes erupt.
  • Sinking convection current in the mantle.
  • Rocks melt and rise.
  • Deep ocean trench forms.
b Why is the Pacific Ocean surrounded by a 'ring of fire'? (What is happening to the Pacific Ocean?)

4 This diagram shows where the main continental blocks were 200 million years ago.

a How did the continental blocks get to their current positions?
b What formed between A and B as they split apart?

1 Copy and complete the following sentences. Use the words below to fill the gaps.

photosynthesis   low   carbon dioxide rate   careful   enzymes   water

- Hazard symbols tell us when to be especially ....

- Catalysts can be used to control the .... of chemical reactions.

- Biological washing powders contain .... to help get clothes clean at .... temperatures.

- Plants use energy from the Sun to make food from .... and .... This is called ....

2 Copy and complete the table to show which of the chemical reactions in the list below are fast and which are slow.

- rusting of metal
- fireworks going off
- an explosion
- silver tarnishing
- coal burning
- oil forming

Slow	Fast

3 The diagram shows two ways that a gardener can supply the nutrients that plants need to grow well.

a List the advantages and disadvantages that each way has for
  i a pensioner growing flowers in pots on the balcony of a flat
  ii a gardener growing food to eat in a small garden at home.
b Only one of these methods is of any use to an organic farmer on a large farm growing cereals. Which is it and why?

2 Safety in the lab

1 Copy and complete the table, showing the names of the pieces of apparatus and what they are used for.

Apparatus	Name	Use
	a	b
	c	d
	e	f
	g	h
	i	j
	k	l

Hazard symbol	Meaning	Example of substance
	a	b
	c	d
	e	f
	g	h
	i	j
	k	l

2 Copy and complete the table (at the top of the next column) showing the meaning of the hazard symbols. Choose an example of a chemical of each type from the list given here.

- lead(II) nitrate
- petrol
- copper(II) oxide
- hydrogen peroxide
- mercury
- hydrochloric acid

3 Hazard symbols are found in many places other than laboratories, including in homes, in garden sheds, in shops and on vehicles. Copy the following table and fill it in, finding as many examples of hazard symbols as you can around your own home. Sometimes the symbols are obvious, sometimes you have to look underneath the bottle or packet to find them. Ask permission before you go searching through the cupboards at home!

Hazard symbol	Where found

1 Copy and complete the following sentences. Use the words below to fill the gaps.

**electricity oxygen shaped hotter
cook energy**

When a fuel burns it reacts with .... in the air. .... is released when this happens, which is transferred to the surroundings, making them ....

Energy from fuels can be used to make ...., to .... food and to work with materials like steel, so that they can be

....

2 When fuels burn in oxygen they produce energy and waste products. Write word equations for the following fuels burning in oxygen.

a charcoal (carbon) + oxygen
   ⟶ ....

b methane (a hydrocarbon) + oxygen
   ⟶ .... + ...

c petrol (a mixture of hydrocarbons) + ...
   ⟶ .... + ...

3 Sherbet is a mixture of sugar and a chemical called sodium hydrogen carbonate. A pupil has an idea that the feeling of 'fizziness' when you put sherbet in your mouth is caused by an endothermic reaction. Design an experiment that the pupil could do to test this idea.

4 In an exothermic reaction energy is 'given out' – transferred to the surroundings. In an endothermic reaction energy is 'taken in' from the surroundings.

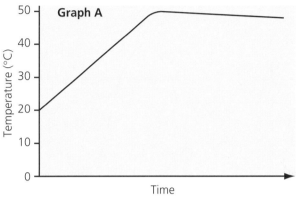

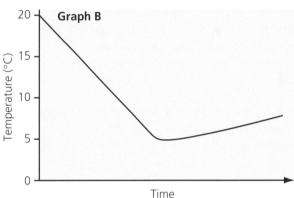

a i Does graph A show an endothermic or an exothermic reaction? How do you know?
  ii Does graph B show an endothermic or an exothermic reaction? How do you know?
b Which of the following chemical changes are exothermic and which are endothermic?
  • a candle burning
  • ammonium chloride dissolving, producing a decrease in temperature
  • dynamite exploding
  • respiration
  • photosynthesis.

4 Making and breaking bonds

1 The amount of energy needed for a reaction to take place is called the activation energy. Copy the diagram, showing the effect of activation energy on a chemical reaction. Use the labels below on your diagram.

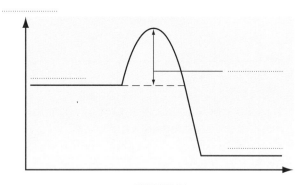

**energy   activation energy   products
course of reaction   reactants**

2 Explain why

a a lower activation energy means a chemical reaction goes faster

b a higher activation energy means a chemical reaction goes slower.

3   a In any chemical reaction energy must be supplied in order to make a chemical reaction happen. What is this energy needed for?

b During a chemical reaction energy is released. What is happening as this energy is released?

c What is happening to the balance of these energy changes in

   i an exothermic reaction

   ii an endothermic reaction?

4 When William and Tanya heat chemical A it decomposes to form chemical B. They then react chemical B with chemical C to form chemical D. The table below gives some information about the energy changes in these chemical reactions.

Chemical reaction	Energy required for bond breaking	Energy released in bond making	Net energy transfer for reaction
A → B	350 kJ/mol	500 kJ/mol	
B + C → D	150 kJ/mol	75 kJ/mol	

a Copy and complete the table.

b What is the overall net energy transfer when chemical A produces chemical D in these two reactions?

5   a Copy and complete the table (at the bottom of the page) showing whether the chemical reactions listed in the table are exothermic or endothermic.

b The energy level diagram for the reaction between ethanol and oxygen is shown below.

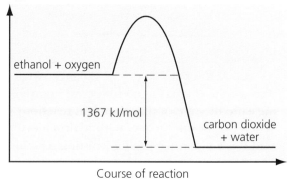

Draw energy level diagrams for the three other reactions from part **a**.

Table for **Q5**

Chemical reaction	ΔH	Exothermic or endothermic?
ethanol + oxygen → carbon dioxide + water	- 1367 kJ/mol	
oxygen → ozone	+ 143 kJ/mol	
nitrogen + hydrogen → hydrazine (rocket fuel)	+ 51 kJ/mol	
magnesium + chlorine → magnesium chloride	- 641 kJ/mol	

1 Copy and complete the following sentences. Use the words below to fill the gaps.

carbon dioxide   wet   raising agent   react tartaric acid

Cakes are light and fluffy because they are made with a .... These only work once the mixture gets .... , when they dissolve and ....

During the reaction between .... and sodium hydrogen carbonate, ... gas is produced and this makes the mixture rise.

2 The diagram shows a conical flask containing hydrochloric acid placed on a top pan balance. Thomas drops a strip of magnesium ribbon into the acid and makes a note of the reading on the balance. The magnesium ribbon fizzes, and eventually dissolves. Thomas notices that the reading on the balance has decreased.

a Why did the reading on the balance decrease?
b As well as the reading on the balance, what else would Thomas need to record in order to measure the rate of this chemical reaction?
c When magnesium reacts with hydrochloric acid it is a vigorous, fizzing, spitting reaction. The decrease in the reading on the balance was very small. Why is it a good idea to include a cotton wool bung in the neck of the flask when carrying out this experiment?

3 The graph (at the top of the next column) shows the rate at which the mass of a flask containing calcium carbonate and hydrochloric acid decreases as the reaction progresses. The flask contains excess hydrochloric acid – that is, there is more than enough acid to react with all the calcium carbonate.

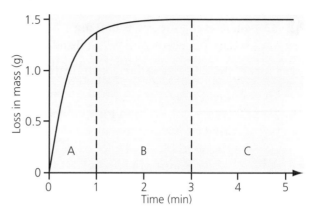

a Why do you think the reaction mixture loses mass as the reaction goes on?
b Explain the shape of the graph in the areas marked A, B and C.

4 Winston, Mona and Sherena carried out an experiment in which they added a piece of magnesium ribbon to hydrochloric acid in a flask on a top pan balance. They timed the loss of mass as the reaction took place and recorded their results in a table.

Time (seconds)	Mass of flask + contents (g)	Total loss of mass (g)
0	170.00	0.00
10	169.96	0.04
20	169.92	0.08
30	169.88	0.12
40	169.85	0.15
50	169.83	0.17
60	169.82	0.18
70	169.81	0.19
80	169.80	0.20
100	169.80	0.20

a Plot a line graph of these results.
b What was the total mass of hydrogen produced in this reaction?
c How long did it take for this hydrogen to be formed?
d Use your answers to parts **b** and **c** to help you work out the average rate of the reaction in g/second.

6 *What affects chemical reactions?*

1 Copy and complete the following sentences. Use the words below to fill the gaps.

pressure double smaller concentration area

The rate of a chemical reaction involving a solid can be increased by making the surface _____ of the solid bigger. This can be done by using _____ lumps of the solid.

If a reaction involves a solution, increasing the _____ of the solution will increase the rate of reaction.

When gases react together, the rate of reaction can be increased by increasing the _____ .

Temperature also affects the rate of a chemical reaction; a 10 °C increase in temperature will roughly _____ the rate of a reaction.

2 Explain the following.

a Small sticks catch fire much more quickly than a big log.
b Food keeps longer in a freezer than in a refrigerator.
c A splint burns steadily in air, but flares up when put into a gas jar of oxygen.
d Advertisers claim that a soluble painkiller acts more quickly than one taken as a tablet.

3 Great care must be taken in sawmills where wood is sawn into planks, since explosions can easily happen if there is a spark or a flame. Use the following statements to help you explain this. Write your answer as complete sentences. You can include the sentences below in your answer if you wish.

• Tiny particles of sawdust spread out through the air.
• An explosion is really just a very rapid burning reaction.
• Sawing wood produces tiny particles of sawdust.
• Wood needs to be heated before it will start to burn.
• The smaller the pieces of solid in a reaction, the faster the reaction.
• Wood burns in air.

4 Sodium thiosulphate reacts with hydrochloric acid, producing a precipitate of sulphur which makes the reacting mixture go cloudy. The table shows how long it takes for a cross marked on a piece of paper under the flask to become invisible. The same concentration of reactants was used in each case.

Temperature (°C)	Time for cross to become invisible
15	200
25	100
35	50
45	25
55	12.5

a Plot a graph of these results.
b What does your graph show about the effect of temperature on the time it takes for the cross to disappear?
c What does this tell us about the effect of temperature on the rate of the reaction?
d Why does temperature have this effect on the rate of a reaction?

7 Catalysts and enzymes

1 Copy and complete the following sentences, choosing the correct ending in each case.

a A catalyst is a substance.....
b An enzyme is.....
c The activation energy of a reaction is.....
d Chemical reactions can only happen when.....
e Concentration, surface area and temperature can all affect.....

Choose the endings from:
- .....the minimum amount of energy particles must have to react.
- .....the rate of a chemical reaction.
- .....reacting particles collide with one another.
- .....that can speed up the rate of a chemical reaction.
- .....a biological catalyst.

2 Copy and complete the following sentences. Use the words below to fill the gaps.

affected protein lower enzymes rate faster metals

Catalysts increase the _____ of a chemical reaction without altering anything else. They can be used to make a reaction go _____ , or they can be used to make a reaction happen at a _____ temperature. They are not _____ themselves and can be used time after time.

Catalysts are often _____ . In living cells special biological catalysts called _____ control all the chemical reactions which go on. Enzymes are made of _____ .

3 Look at the diagram, which shows some metal catalysts used in a chemical reaction.

Explain why the pieces of catalyst have holes in them. Use your knowledge about things that affect the rate of chemical reactions.

4 The graph shows the rate of a chemical reaction which can be catalysed by three different enzymes. One is a bacterium which lives in hot springs, another is a mammal, and the third is a fish which lives in Arctic waters.

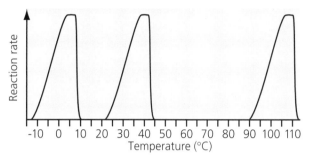

a Copy the graph and label it clearly to show which enzyme comes from which living thing.
b All three lines showing enzyme activity have very similar shapes. Explain what the shape tells us about how enzymes work.

5 **a** Copy and complete these activation energy diagrams, using the following labels (you may use each label more than once).
- reactants
- activation energy (without catalyst)
- energy
- course of reaction
- activation energy (with catalyst)
- products

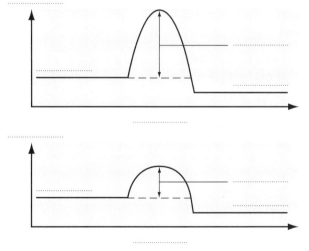

b Use your labelled diagrams to explain how a catalyst speeds up a chemical reaction.

8 Enzymes – the enablers

1 Copy and complete the following sentences. Use the words below to fill the gaps.

**bread   carbon dioxide   yoghurt
alcoholic   sugar   fungus**

Yeast is a _____ . Yeast cells break down sugar to produce _____ and ethanol. Yeast is used to make _____ rise, and to make _____ drinks. _____ is produced from milk using bacteria. The bacteria convert _____ in the milk into lactic acid, which gives a sharp taste.

2 The picture shows two packets of washing powder.

a Describe the main difference between the contents of the two packets.
b The packets have the following statements printed on them:
   • Packet A – This washing powder is effective at all temperatures.
   • Packet B – For washing clothes at low temperatures.
   Which packet is which? Explain your answer.

3 Sarah and Alice are investigating the effect of temperature on the activity of yeast. They set up three test tubes in three separate water baths, at 20 °C, 40 °C and 60 °C. Each test tube contained a mixture of yeast, sugar and water. They recorded their observations in a table.

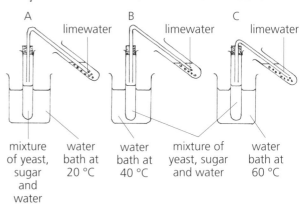

Temperature of water bath (°C)	Amount of bubbling	Time taken for the limewater to turn cloudy (mins)
20	bubbles gradually built up to a gentle stream	10
40	quickly produced lots of bubbles	2.5
60	few bubbles at first, then none	stayed clear

a Explain what happened in test tubes A, B and C.
b What does this tell you about enzyme-controlled reactions?

4 When yeast cells break down sugar, energy is released into the surroundings as heat. In breweries, this heat is removed from the huge brewing vessels used to make beer by using water which flows through a system of pipes. In home brewing, however, the fermenting mixture containing the yeast must be kept in a warm place (often the airing cupboard). Explain this difference.

9 Chemistry for farmers

1 Copy and complete the following sentences. Choose the correct word from each of the pairs given.

Growing plants use energy from sunlight to make food from carbon dioxide and water – this is called **photosynthesis/catalysis**. Plants also need **reactants/minerals** from the soil in order to grow properly. They use nitrates from the soil to make **proteins/sugars**. Nitrates can be put back into the soil using manure or compost, but artificial **crops/fertilisers** provide a more concentrated source of nitrates. If large amounts of nitrates get into ponds and streams they may cause **eutrophication / oxygenation**. The nitrates make plants grow quickly, and the water becomes choked with plants which then die and rot, using up all the **oxygen/nitrogen** in the water.

2 'Forests grow perfectly well without artificial fertilisers, yet farmers need to fertilise fields in which they grow crops year after year.' Use the diagram of the nitrogen cycle to help you explain why this is.

3 Artificial fertilisers have done a lot of good but they have caused problems as well.

a What is the main benefit of using artificial fertilisers?
b One of the main problems which results from artificial fertilisers finding their way into ponds, streams and rivers is eutrophication. Explain what happens when a stream is affected by eutrophication.
c Give one further problem which can result from the use of nitrate fertilisers.

4 Nitrate fertilisers are very commonly used by farmers to provide their crop plants with the nitrates that they need.

a Why can't plants get the nitrates they need from the nitrogen in the air?
b Ammonium nitrate fertiliser is made by reacting ammonia with nitric acid. What kind of reaction is this?
c Write a word equation for the reaction.

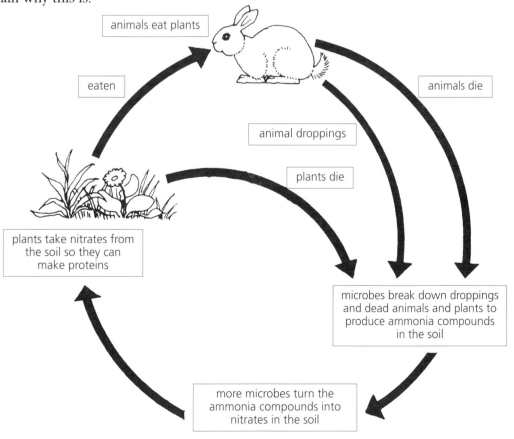

animals eat plants

eaten

animals die

animal droppings

plants die

plants take nitrates from the soil so they can make proteins

microbes break down droppings and dead animals and plants to produce ammonia compounds in the soil

more microbes turn the ammonia compounds into nitrates in the soil

1 Complete the following sentences, choosing the correct ending in each case. Then, rearrange the sentences to describe the production of ammonia. Copy the sentences out in the correct order.

- The main ingredient of any nitrate fertiliser is.....
- The raw ingredients of the Haber process are.....
- Ammonia.....
- Nitrogen is unreactive so the Haber process needs.....
- The nitrogen comes from the air.....
- The process also uses a moderately high.....

Choose the endings from:
- .....an iron catalyst.
- .....temperature and pressure.
- .....and the hydrogen comes from methane.
- .....is made by the Haber process.
- .....ammonia.
- .....nitrogen and hydrogen.

2 Copy the diagram of the Haber process. Use the labels below in place of letters A–F on your diagram.

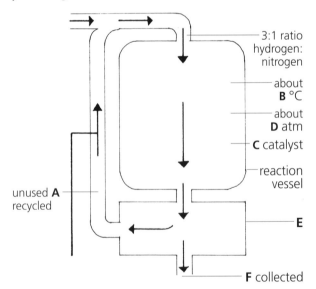

- iron
- liquid ammonia
- 200
- hydrogen and nitrogen
- condenser
- 450

3 **a** Give a word equation for the Haber process.
b Give two ways in which the ammonia produced in the Haber process may be used.

4 Plants need nitrates to grow well, but they cannot use the nitrogen in the air. Farmers often supply their crops with extra nitrates using artificial fertilisers.

a What is the main ingredient of ammonium nitrate fertiliser?
b Why is the Haber process so important in the production of large amounts of cheap fertiliser?
c Explain why we need large amounts of cheap fertiliser all over the world.

5 The graph shows how the temperature and pressure in the Haber process affects the yield of ammonia.

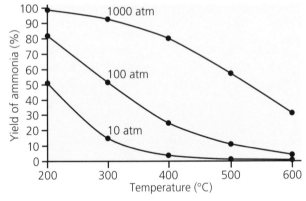

a What is the yield of ammonia at 300 °C and at
  i 10 atm pressure
  ii 100 atm pressure
  iii 1000 atm pressure?
b From the graph, which conditions seem to give the best yield of ammonia?
c Why are these *not* the normal operating conditions for the Haber process in industry?
d The normal operating conditions for the Haber process are around 450 °C and 200 atm pressure. What do you think the yield of ammonia is likely to be using these conditions?
e Why are the conditions described in part **d** used for the industrial Haber process?

11 The best conditions

1 Chemical plants have to be run to make a profit, so the reactions need to run as quickly and efficiently as possible. Complete the table to give four factors which affect the rates of reaction. For each factor give an explanation of how it works.

Factor affecting rate of reaction	How it works

2 **a** Write down the balanced chemical equation which describes the equilibrium which occurs when nitrogen and hydrogen react to produce ammonia.

b How many moles of gas are there on the left-hand side of the equilibrium?

c How many moles of gas are there on the right-hand side of the equilibrium?

d Does an increase in pressure increase or decrease the yield of products on the right-hand side of the equation?

e The usual operating pressure for the commercial production of ammonia is about 200 atm. Why do you think this has been chosen, rather than a higher or lower pressure?

3 Bloggs and Son are looking into setting up a business to make chemical Z. Z is made when chemical X decomposes to Y and Z in the following reaction. All three are gases.

$$X \rightleftharpoons Y + Z$$

a What does the sign $\rightleftharpoons$ tell you about the reaction?

b 'If the reaction is allowed to take place in a closed vessel, equilibrium is reached.' What does this mean?

c Mr Bloggs wants to make sure that he gets lots of chemical Z, and certainly does not want the reaction to go into reverse and make chemical X again. What can he do to make sure that he gets as much Z as possible?

4 The diagram shows some apparatus that can be used to decompose ammonia into unreactive nitrogen and inflammable hydrogen.

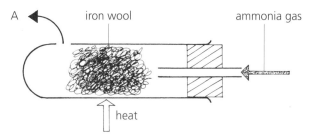

a What is the purpose of the iron wool?

b Most of the ammonia decomposes. Explain why.

c Suggest one simple chemical test to detect undecomposed ammonia in the stream of gases at A.

d How could hydrogen be removed from the mixture of gases leaving A?

12 Calculating chemicals

Use the information below to help you answer these questions.

Element	Symbol	Relative atomic mass (A_r)
calcium	Ca	40
carbon	C	12
chlorine	Cl	35.5
copper	Cu	64
fluorine	F	19
hydrogen	H	1
iron	Fe	56
magnesium	Mg	24
nitrogen	N	14
oxygen	O	16
phosphorus	P	31
sodium	Na	23
sulphur	S	32

1 Copy and complete the following sentences. Use the words below to fill the gaps.

relative atomic mass   react   compound elements

The atoms of different .... all have different masses. So that we know how the masses of different atoms compare with each other we use their .... (A_r).

Then we can work out the relative formula mass (M_r) of a .... , which is very useful when we are measuring out substances to .... together.

2 The relative formula mass of a compound is found by adding together the relative atomic masses of all the atoms in a molecule of the compound. Calculate the relative formula mass of each of the following substances. For example:

water, H_2O 2 x A_r of hydrogen = 2 x 1 = 2

1 x A_r of oxygen = 1 x 16 = 16

So the M_r of water is 2 + 16 = 18

a ammonia, NH_3
b magnesium chloride, $MgCl_2$
c copper sulphate, $CuSO_4$
d ethanol, C_2H_5OH

3 a Work out the relative formula mass of the following substances.

CO	Fe	CaH_2	PH_3
N_2H_4	H_2O_2	CH_3OH	N_2
H_2CO_3	NaF	CaO	MgF_2

b Put the substances from part **a** into pairs with the same relative formula mass.

4 a Ammonium nitrate, NH_4NO_3, and ammonium phosphate, $(NH_4)_2HPO_4$, are both artificial fertilisers. Calculate the percentage of nitrogen in each fertiliser.
b Farmer John Smith found the yield of his cereal crop was lower than usual last year. The plants showed the symptoms of a lack of nitrates. If he used the same amount of each of these two fertilisers, which would be most effective for improving the crop yield? Explain your answer.

5 The relative atomic mass in grams of any element contains 6.02 x 10^{23} atoms. For example, 12 g of carbon contains 6.02 x 10^{23} atoms, while 6.02 x 10^{23} atoms of hydrogen have a mass of 1 g. Calculate the number of atoms in the following.
a 23 g of sodium   d 60 g of magnesium
b 355 g of chlorine   e 0.06 g of carbon
c 6.4 g of sulphur

13 How much and how many?

Use the information below to help you answer these questions.

Element	Symbol	Relative atomic mass (A_r)
aluminium	Al	27
carbon	C	12
chlorine	Cl	35.5
copper	Cu	64
fluorine	F	19
hydrogen	H	1
iron	Fe	56
magnesium	Mg	24
oxygen	O	16
phosphorus	P	31
potassium	K	39
sodium	Na	23
sulphur	S	32

1 We know that the mass of any chemical equals the number of moles present multiplied by the mass of 1 mole. Put another way

the number of moles of a chemical

$$= \frac{\text{the mass of the chemical}}{\text{the mass of 1 mole of the chemical}}$$

Use this equation to calculate the number of moles in the following compounds.

a 62 g of Na_2O
b 22 g of CO_2
c 5.8 g of KF
d 30 g of $MgSO_4$
e 6.75 g of $CuCl_2$

2 Powdered aluminium and iron(III) oxide react vigorously according to the following equation:

$$Al + Fe_2O_3 \longrightarrow Al_2O_3 + Fe$$

a Balance this equation.
b In one reaction, 5 moles of aluminium were mixed with 2 moles of iron(III) oxide. How many grams of iron metal could be produced using these quantities of reactants?

3 Phosphoric acid, H_3PO_4, is used to make phosphate fertilisers. Phosphoric acid can be made by boiling phosphorus oxide, P_4O_{10}, with water.

$$P_4O_{10} + H_2O \longrightarrow H_3PO_4$$

a Balance this equation.
b If 14.2 g of P_4O_{10} were reacted with water how much phosphoric acid was formed
  i in moles
  ii in grams?

4 Sodium carbonate, Na_2CO_3, is an important chemical used in many industrial processes. It is made from salt, using a method called the Solvay process. The Solvay process has two steps:

1 $H_2O + NaCl + NH_3 + CO_2 \longrightarrow NH_4Cl + NaHCO_3$

2 $2NaHCO_3 \longrightarrow Na_2CO_3 + CO_2 + H_2O$

a Rewrite the first equation to show the quantities of all the chemicals which would have to react to give $2NaHCO_3$ as one of the products.
b How many moles of sodium carbonate could be made from 100 moles of salt?
c How many moles of carbon dioxide are required when 4 moles of salt react to form sodium carbonate?
d How many grams of salt would be needed to make 31.8 g of sodium carbonate using the Solvay process?

14 Finding the formula

Use the information below to help you answer these questions.

Element	Symbol	Relative atomic mass (A_r)
bromine	Br	80
chlorine	Cl	35.5
copper	Cu	64
iron	Fe	56
oxygen	O	16
sodium	Na	23
sulphur	S	32
vanadium	V	51

1 The diagram shows the electrolysis of copper chloride.

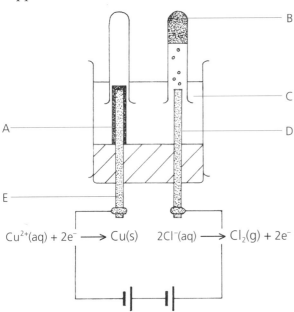

$$Cu^{2+}(aq) + 2e^- \longrightarrow Cu(s) \qquad 2Cl^-(aq) \longrightarrow Cl_2(g) + 2e^-$$

a Copy and complete the diagram, labelling the parts A–E.
b Explain in words what is happening at the two electrodes.
c Give one industrial use of this type of electrolysis.

2 When liquid sodium chloride is electrolysed, the half-equations are:

$$Na^+(l) + e^- \longrightarrow Na(l)$$

$$2Cl^-(l) \longrightarrow Cl_2(g) + 2e^-$$

a Copy out these half-equations and balance them so they both involve the same number of electrons.
b If an electrolysis cell produces 11.5 g of sodium metal, how many grams of chlorine gas will be produced?

3 A solution of copper bromide is electrolysed. After passing electricity through the solution, it is found that 5.12 g of copper and 12.8 g of bromine have been produced.

a Calculate the empirical formula of copper bromide.
b Write the symbols for a copper ion and a bromide ion.
c Write half-equations for the reactions going on at the cathode and anode.

4 Vanadium is a metal used in nuclear reactors. Patronite is an ore which contains vanadium combined with sulphur as vanadium sulphide. If 3.58 g of patronite contain 1.02 g of vanadium, what is the empirical formula of patronite?

5 Magnetite is an ore of iron which contains 72.4% by mass of iron, the rest being oxygen. What is the empirical formula of magnetite?

1 Copy and complete the following sentences. Use the words below to fill the gaps.

gases particles squashed closer solids

Everything is made up of tiny .... In .... and liquids, these particles are close together, so solids and liquids cannot be .... In ...., these particles are far apart. When you squash a gas, you push the particles .... together.

2 Copy and complete this table, writing **fixed** or **not fixed** in the missing slots.

	Shape	Volume
solid	**a**	fixed
liquid	**b**	fixed
gas	not fixed	**c**

3 **a** Copy these three diagrams, showing how the particles are arranged in solids, liquids and gases. Label them as solid, liquid or gas, as appropriate.

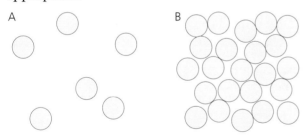

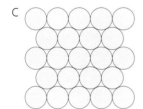

b Which has the most ordered arrangement?
c Which has the biggest gap between the particles?
d In which are the particles held firmly in place?
e In which two are the particles free to move?
f In which are the particles the most free to move?

4 The diagram shows how the particles are arranged in solid iron and solid lead. The forces holding the iron particles together are stronger than the forces holding the lead particles together.

Iron   **Lead**

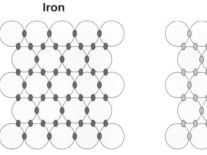 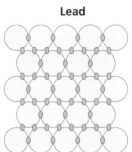

⊙ represent the forces holding the
⬤ particles together

Copy and complete the following sentences, choosing the correct ending in each case.
a Solids like iron and lead keep their shape because.....
b Iron is harder and stronger than lead because.....
c Lead is heavier for its size than iron because.....

Choose the endings from:
• .....the forces between the particles in iron are stronger than in lead.
• .....lead particles weigh more than iron particles.
• .....the particles are held in place by forces.

5 In every substance, it is as if there is a battle going on between forces that hold the particles together and movement which tries to tear them apart. Copy and complete the following sentences, choosing the correct ending in each case.

a In a solid..... **b** In a liquid..... **c** In a gas.....

Choose the endings from:
• .....it is evenly balanced. The forces still keep the particles together, but they can slip and slide over one another.
• .....motion has won! The particles have broken free and are whizzing about at high speed.
• .....the forces are winning. The particles can only vibrate in their fixed places.

1 a Rearrange these sentences to explain how ice turns to water as it is heated. Copy the sentences out in the correct order.

- As ice is heated, the particles vibrate faster and faster.
- The ice melts.
- At 0 °C, the particles are vibrating fast enough to start snapping the force bonds that hold them together.
- In solid ice, the particles are vibrating about fixed positions.

b What is the melting point of ice?

c Sulphur melts at 113 °C. Do you think the forces between sulphur particles are stronger or weaker than those between water particles in ice? Explain your answer.

2 a Rearrange these sentences to explain how steam turns to water as it is cools. Copy the sentences out in the correct order.

- At or below 100 °C, the particles stick together if they collide.
- The water particles in steam are far apart and moving very fast.
- The steam condenses.
- If the particles collide they simply bounce apart again.
- Clumps of particles stick together and collect, forming liquid water droplets.
- As the steam cools, the particles slow down.

b Alcohol vapour only condenses if the temperature drops below 77 °C. Do you think the forces between alcohol particles are stronger or weaker than between water particles in steam? Explain your answer.

c Explain what happens to the particles in water if they are heated to 100 °C.

3 Dr Martin played a nasty trick on his class. He let off a stink bomb at the front without telling them. He timed how long it took for different pupils to notice.

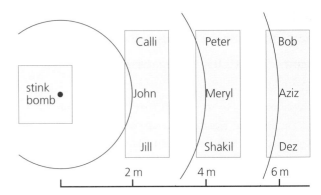

Here are his results:
John   (10 seconds)   Shakil (23 seconds)
Calli   (16 seconds)   Aziz   (29 seconds)
Meryl (20 seconds)   Bob   (33 seconds)

a How did the 'smell particles' reach the pupils.

b Explain briefly how this works.

c Why did John notice first?

d Plot a graph of distance in metres against time in seconds for the smell to travel. (Estimate distance from the circles.) Draw a line of best fit.

e Use this to estimate the 'time of arrival' of the smell to Jill, Peter and Dez.

f How fast did the smell diffuse through the class (in metres per second)? (speed = distance/time).

4 a Copy the diagram, which shows how salt dissolves in water. Use the sentences below to label the diagram.

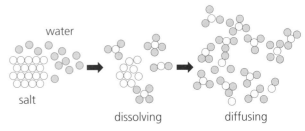

- The salt and water particles diffuse away, allowing more salt particles to be freed, and so on.
- Some of the outer salt particles are jostled free.
- Water particles surround the salt crystal.

b Is this diffusion faster or slower than in a gas? Explain your answer.

1 Copy and complete the following sentences. Use the words below to fill the gaps.

compound   different   atoms   element

All substances are made from .... There are over 90 .... kinds of atom. A substance made from one kind of atom only is called an .... A substance made from two or more different types of atoms joined together is called a ....

2 Most elements have symbols of one or two letters based on their name.

a Copy out the name of each element and write its symbol beside it. (Look for the clue!)
- **H**ydrogen
- **C**arbon
- **N**itrogen
- **O**xygen
- **Br**omine
- **Al**uminium
- **Ca**lcium
- **He**lium
- **Zn**c
- **Cl**orine
- **Mg**nesium

b Why can't helium just be H, or chlorine just C?

3 The symbols Na, K, Fe, Pb, Ag, Cu and Au are based on the old names of the elements. From this list, which symbol represents each of the following elements? Copy out the current name of each element and write its symbol beside it.

- Iron was called ferrum.
- Silver was called argentum.
- Lead was called plumbum.
- Copper was called cuprum.
- Sodium was called natrium.
- Gold was called aurum.
- Potassium was called kalium.

4 When elements combine to form new compounds, the compound name often tells you which elements have combined. For example, sulphur dioxide is a compound made from sulphur and oxygen atoms. In this case, the name *di*oxide also tells you that there are *two* oxygen atoms present. This can be shown in a diagram, or by the chemical formula, SO_2.

For each of the following simple compounds, match up the name to its diagram and formula. (Alternative names have been given where the common name does not follow the simple rules.)

Copy and complete the following table.

Compound	Diagram	Formula
hydrogen chloride	a	b
carbon dioxide	c	d
carbon monoxide	e	f
ammonia (*nitrogen trihydride*)	g	h
water (*dihydrogen oxide*)	i	j

Choose from the following diagrams and formulae:

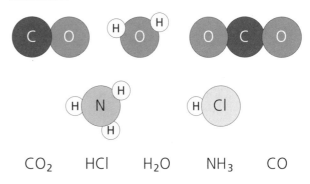

CO_2 HCl H_2O NH_3 CO

5 For each of the following compounds, write down which elements make up the compound and how many of each type are there.

a Methane, CH_4 (natural gas)
b Octane, C_8H_{18} (in petrol)
c Glucose, $C_6H_{12}O_6$
d Sulphuric acid, H_2SO_4
e Nitric acid, HNO_3

6 These compounds and their formulae have been mixed up. Match the correct formula to each compound and then copy them out.

- calcium carbonate
- sodium chloride
- aluminium oxide
- lead bromide

- $PbBr_2$
- Al_2O_3
- NaCl
- $CaCO_3$

1 Copy and complete the following sentences. Use the words below to fill the gaps.

ions   carbon   metals   molecules

Compounds made from non-metallic elements such as ...., hydrogen and oxygen form uncharged particles called .... When .... form compounds with non-metals, however, they form ionic compounds which involve charged particles called ....

2 Carbon and oxygen (the reactants) combine to give carbon dioxide (the product).

a Draw a table with two columns. Label the first column 'Reactants' and the second 'Products'. For each of the following reactions, put the substances in the correct columns.

A If you burn hydrogen in oxygen you get water.

B When magnesium reacts with sulphuric acid you get magnesium sulphate and hydrogen.

C Rust is a form of iron oxide which you get when iron reacts with oxygen in the air.

D If you heat copper carbonate you get copper oxide and carbon dioxide.

b Write out each reaction as a word equation, in the form:
carbon + oxygen ⟶ carbon dioxide.

3 Different atoms can make different numbers of bonds. The diagram shows how you can use a simple 'handshake' model to work out the formula of some simple compounds between metals and non-metals.

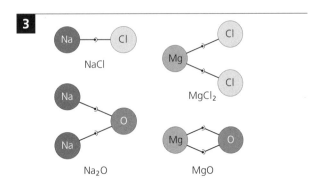

3

NaCl

MgCl₂

Na₂O

MgO

a Potassium (K) has one bond 'arm', while calcium (Ca) has two. Use this idea to work out the formulae of
i potassium chloride
ii potassium oxide
iii calcium chloride
iv calcium oxide.
b Lithium chloride has the formula LiCl. How many bond 'arms' does lithium have?
c Lead chloride has the formula PbCl₂. How many bond 'arms' does lead have here?
d Sodium bromide is NaBr, while magnesium bromide is MgBr₂. How many bond 'arms' does bromine (Br) have here?

Some metals can vary the number of bonds they can make. For example, iron can have two, written as iron(II), or three, written as iron(III).

e What are the formulae of
i iron(II) chloride
ii iron(III) chloride
iii copper(I) oxide
iv copper(II) oxide?

4 Copy and complete this sentence. Choose the correct word from each of the pairs given. You should be able to do this in two different ways, to make *two* correct sentences.

The charge on a **metallic / non-metallic** ion is **negative / positive.**

5 Look at the following balanced chemical equations. For each, write out the reaction as a word equation.

a $2Mg(s) + O_2(g) \longrightarrow 2MgO(s)$
b $Na_2O(s) + 2HCl(aq) \longrightarrow 2NaCl(aq) + H_2O(l)$
c $CuO(s) + H_2SO_4(aq) \longrightarrow CuSO_4(aq) + H_2O(l)$
d $2Al(s) + Fe_2O_3(s) \longrightarrow 2Fe(l) + Al_2O_3(s)$
e $Mg(s) + 2HCl(aq) \longrightarrow MgCl_2(aq) + H_2(g)$
f $2Na(s) + 2H_2O(l) \longrightarrow 2NaOH(aq) + H_2(g)$
g The symbol (aq) means in solution in water (from the latin for water, which is *aqua*). What do you think (s), (l) and (g) mean? Write down your answers.

5 Inside the atom

1 Copy and complete the following sentences. Use the words below to fill the gaps.

nucleus subatomic electrons protons

Atoms are made from even smaller .... particles. In the centre is the .... , which contains the .... and neutrons. The shape of the atom is given by tiny particles called .... , which whizz around the nucleus.

2 **a** Copy and complete this sentence. Choose the correct word from each of the pairs given. You should be able to do this in two different ways, to make *two* correct sentences.

Protons / Electrons have a relatively **large / small** mass and a **negative / positive** charge.

b What is the charge on a neutron? (Think!)
c Which two particles are found in the nucleus?
d Draw a simple diagram of a section through an atom, showing the nucleus, protons, neutrons and electrons.

3 The mass of a proton is too small to measure in grams. Instead the mass is compared to a hydrogen atom, which is given the value 1. Copy and complete this table, showing the relative mass and charge of the subatomic particles.

	Mass	Charge
Proton	**a**	positive
Neutron	1	**b**
Electron	0	**c**

4 Copy and complete the following sentences. Choose the correct word from each of the pairs.

Atoms of the same element have the same number of **protons / neutrons**. The number of **protons / neutrons** in an atom is called its **atomic / mass** number (Z). The number of protons plus the number of **electrons / neutrons** gives the **atomic / mass** number (A). As an atom is neutral, the number of negative **electrons / neutrons** is always the same as the number of positive protons.

5 For each of the following elements, give the atomic number (proton number, Z) and the mass number (A).

a Helium (He) has 2 protons, 2 neutrons and 2 electrons.
b Fluorine (F) has 9 protons, 10 neutrons and 9 electrons.
c Iron (Fe) has 26 protons, 30 neutrons and 26 electrons.
d Uranium (U) has 92 protons, 146 neutrons and 92 electrons.

6 Copy and complete this table, showing the subatomic particles in the following elements.

Element	Number of...			Mass number
	Protons	Neutrons	Electrons	
Li	**a**	4	**b**	7
Na	**c**	**d**	11	23
Kr	36	**e**	**f**	84
Pb	**g**	**h**	82	207

7 Chlorine comes in two forms, $^{35}_{17}Cl$ and $^{37}_{17}Cl$.

a How do you know that they are both the same element?
b What is the difference between the two versions, or *isotopes*, of chlorine?
c Which element is X an isotope of? Explain your answer. $^{12}_{6}C$ $^{14}_{6}X$ $^{14}_{7}N$

8 **a** Write down the proton number (Z) and mass number (A) for the first 10 elements. (Use the Periodic Table on page 169). Calculate the number of neutrons for each of the first 10 elements.
b Plot a graph of the number of neutrons (on the y-axis) against the number of protons (on the x-axis). Draw a line of best fit.
c What is the approximate relationship between the number of protons and the number of neutrons for the first 10 elements?
d Does this simple relationship hold for larger atoms such as uranium ($^{238}_{92}U$) and lead ($^{207}_{82}Pb$)? Explain your answer.

1 Copy and complete the following sentences. Use the words below to fill the gaps.

eight   shell   electrons   energy

The .... in an atom are not free to move where they like. They can only occur in fixed electron .... positions (.................... levels). The first shell can only take two electrons, while the second shell can take up to .... electrons.

2 Match the following elements to their electron shell diagrams. Write each element's name, number and electron shell pattern in the following form:

calcium ($^{40}_{20}$Ca) 2,8,8,2

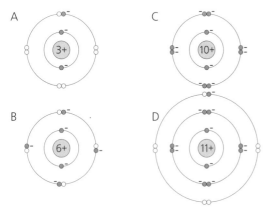

neon ($^{20}_{10}$Ne)   sodium ($^{23}_{11}$Na)
carbon ($^{12}_{6}$C)   lithium ($^{7}_{3}$Li)

3 On diagrams like the ones in **Q2**, draw the electron positions for boron (5), oxygen (8), magnesium (12), argon (18) and potassium (19).

4 Metals have just a small number of electrons in the outer shell, which they lose to form positive ions. Non-metals have a small number of gaps in their outer electron shell, which they fill to make negative ions.

a Copy and complete this table.

Atomic number (Z)	Metal or non-metal	Atom			Ion	
8	i	O	2,6	→	O^{2-}	ii
11	iii	Na	2,8,1	→	Na$^+$	iv
12	metal	Mg	2,8,2	→	Mg^{2+} 2,8	
17	non-metal	Cl	2,8,7	→	Cl$^-$ 2,8,8	
20	v	Ca	vi	→	Ca^{2+}	vii

b What do you notice about the electron structure of:
   i oxygen, sodium and magnesium ions?
   ii chlorine and calcium ions?
c What is different about the ions?
d Metals and non-metals form ionic compounds. From the table in part **a**, explain why:
   i sodium chloride is NaCl, but magnesium chloride is MgCl$_2$;
   ii calcium oxide is CaO, but sodium oxide is Na$_2$O.

5 **a** Look at this diagram of the giant ionic structure of a crystal of common salt, sodium chloride (NaCl). Which of the sentences below could be used to replace the letters A–C? Copy the sentences out in the order A–C, to explain how the crystal is formed.

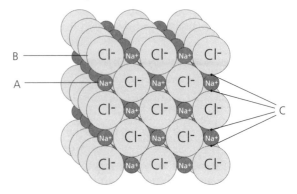

• Chlorine atoms have gained an electron to become Cl$^-$.
• Sodium atoms have lost an electron to become Na$^+$.
• Opposite charges attract to form a giant ionic structure.

b Why does salt have high melting and boiling points?

7 *More about chemical bonds*

1 Look at the electron shell diagrams for atoms of the three unreactive gases helium ($_2$He), neon ($_{10}$Ne) and argon ($_{18}$Ar).

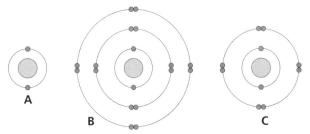

a Copy out the three diagrams and name them.
b What have the three atoms got in common?
c A full outer shell gives great stability. What chemical property does this give to these three gases?
d Draw an electron shell diagram for a sodium ($Z = 11$) ion, Na$^+$.
e Draw an electron shell diagram for a fluorine ($Z = 9$) ion, F$^-$.
f What do you notice about your diagrams for parts **d** and **e**? Which unreactive gas are they like?
g Suggest a reason why sodium and fluorine atoms form ions like this.
h What is the difference between the sodium and fluorine ions?

2 The electron configuration of sodium can be written as Na 2,8,1.

a What part of this tells you that sodium is a metal?
b What must sodium do to form an ion?
c Chlorine can be written as Cl 2,8,7. What part of this tells you that chlorine is a non-metal?
d Rearrange these sentences to explain how sodium and chlorine atoms combine to form sodium chloride. Copy the sentences out in the correct order.
  • An ionic bond is formed, making sodium chloride.
  • The oppositely charged ions are attracted to each other.
  • The chlorine atom accepts the electron.
  • It becomes a negative ion.
  • The sodium atom donates its 'loose' electron and becomes a positive ion.

3 The electron configuration of calcium can be written as Ca 2,8,8,2.

a How do you know that calcium is a metal?
b What must it do to form an ion?
c What will the charge on the ion be?
d How many chlorine ions could be made using the outer electrons from one calcium atom?
e From your answer to part **d**, what must the formula of calcium chloride be?
f Draw electron shell diagrams to show how calcium chloride could be formed.

4 **a** Copy the diagram below and use the idea of sharing to explain how chlorine atoms can join together to form a Cl$_2$ molecule.

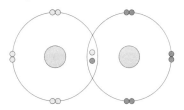

b What is this kind of bond called?
c The diagram above shows just the outer electron shells. The diagram below, a 'dot and cross' diagram, shows the outer shell electrons from one atom as 'dots' and from the other as 'crosses'.

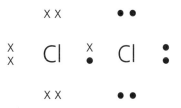

Draw a 'dot and cross' diagram to show how an F$_2$ fluorine molecule could form ($Z = 9$).
d Oxygen is O 2,6. How many electron pairs will oxygen need to share to form a covalent O$_2$ molecule?
e Draw a 'dot and cross' diagram for an O$_2$ molecule.

Draw 'dot and cross' diagrams for
f water, H$_2$O (H = 1, O = 8)
g ammonia, NH$_3$ (N = 7)
h methane, CH$_4$ (C = 6)
i carbon dioxide, CO$_2$
(There are only two electrons in the first shell.)

8 *The structure of materials*

1 Copy and complete the following sentences. Use the words below to fill the gaps.

molecules giant covalent high low weak strong

Although .... bonds are very strong, the forces between covalent molecules are .... Because of this, substances with small .... such as methane or ammonia have very .... melting and boiling points.

However, some covalent materials, such as diamond or silicon dioxide, form .... structures. Because every bond in these materials is a .... covalent bond, they are hard solids with .... melting and boiling points.

2 Look at the diagrams of diamond and graphite.

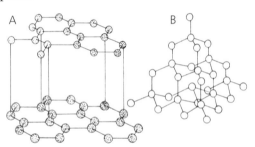

a Copy and complete: A is ...., B is ....

b What is the same about these two giant structures, and what is different?
c Explain why both diamond and graphite have very high melting points.
d Explain why diamond is very hard, but graphite is very soft.

3 Ionic compounds such as sodium chloride form giant structures.

a What force holds the ions together in sodium chloride?
b What properties does this give ionic solids?
c Ionic substances are made of charged particles. Why do they not conduct electricity when they are solid?
d What are the two ways that the ions can be freed up, so that the ionic material can conduct?

e We write the formula of the compound sodium chloride as NaCl. Does such a unit actually exist? Explain your answer.

4 Copy this diagram of a metallic giant structure.

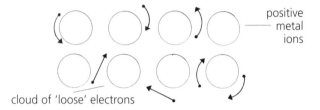

positive metal ions

cloud of 'loose' electrons

a How does this explain the hardness and high melting point of most metals?
b How does it explain the fact that solid metals conduct electricity?
c How does it explain the fact that metals can be easily shaped without breaking?

5 Look at the following table of data about some different substances.

Name	mp (°C)	bp (°C)	Electrical conductivity
aluminium oxide	2072	2980	poor (s), good (l)
ammonia	-77	-34	poor
calcium chloride	782	1600	poor (s), good (l)
carbon dioxide	–	-78	poor
diamond	3550	4830	poor
iron	1535	3000	good
silicon dioxide	1610	2230	poor
silver	961	2210	good

Draw a table with four headings:
Ionic Molecular Metallic Giant molecular
a Under each heading, write whether you would expect to see high or low melting and boiling points.
b Write whether you would expect a solid to conduct electricity.
c Write whether you would expect a liquid to conduct electricity.
d Write the name of each substance from the table above under the appropriate heading.

9 Ordering the elements

1 Copy and complete the following sentences. Use the words below to fill the gaps.

similar elements different repeating

When the first 20 _____ are listed in order of atomic number (Z), they show a _____ pattern of properties. Elements next to one another are often very _____ , but elements with _____ properties appear after a count of 8.

2 Copy out the table of elements.

Z	A	Element	Properties
1	1	hydrogen	a very reactive gas
2	4	helium	an inert (unreactive) gas
3	7	lithium	a soft, very reactive metal
4	9	beryllium	a reactive metal
5	11	boron	a solid non-metal
6	12	carbon	a solid non-metal
7	14	nitrogen	a non-metal
8	16	oxygen	a reactive non-metal
9	19	fluorine	a very reactive non-metal (gas)
10	20	neon	?
11	23	sodium	?
12	24	magnesium	a reactive metal
13	27	aluminium	a reactive metal
14	28	silicon	?
15	31	phosphorus	a non-metal
16	32	sulphur	?
17	35.5	chlorine	?
18	40	argon	an inert (unreactive) gas
19	39	potassium	a soft, very reactive metal
20	40	calcium	?

a Use the 'count to 8' rule to fill in the missing properties.

b This pattern is good, but not perfect. What is odd about elements number 5 and 13?

c Originally, the elements were ordered by increasing atomic mass. Which element would be 'out of position' if you did this?

d When Newlands first noticed this pattern in 1864, this anomaly didn't bother him. Why not? (Clue: the family of unreactive gases was discovered in 1892.)

3 **a** Copy out this simple version of the Periodic Table. Put the missing element symbols in their correct places. Choose from Ca, He, S, C, F and Mg. Use **Q2** to help you.

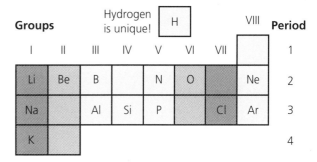

b What do all the elements in
  i Group I have in common?
  ii Group VII have in common?
  iii Group VIII have in common?

c What is the name of the element with the symbol **i** Na? **ii** K?

4 Redraw your simple version of the Periodic Table from **Q3**. Use the sentences below to annotate it, to explain the link between the structure of the Periodic Table and electron shells.

A The group number tells you how many electrons there are in the outer shell.

B Helium is usually put in Group VIII with the noble gases as its two electrons still give it a full outer shell.

C The period number of an element tells you how many electron shells it has.

D The first period only has 2 elements because the first shell can only take 2 electrons.

E The higher periods have 8 elements, because these shells can take 8 electrons.

10 The Periodic Table

1 The table below gives the melting points (in °C) of the first 20 elements:

Atomic no.	Element	mp (°C)	Atomic no.	Element	mp (°C)
1	H	-259	11	Na	98
2	He	-272	12	Mg	649
3	Li	181	13	Al	660
4	Be	1278	14	Si	1410
5	B	2300	15	P	44
6	C	3652	16	S	119
7	N	-210	17	Cl	-101
8	O	-218	18	Ar	-189
9	F	-220	19	K	63
10	Ne	-248	20	Ca	839

a By hand or using a computer, plot a graph of melting point against atomic number.
b How many of these elements are solid at room temperature (25 °C)?

You will need to use the table in **Q1** and the Periodic Table (page 169) to answer **Q2** and **Q3**.

2 **a** To what group do elements number 2, 10 and 18 belong?
b Are these elements metals or non-metals?
c What do you notice about the melting points of elements 2, 10, and 18?
d To what group do elements number 6 and 14 belong?
e Are these elements metals or non-metals?
f What do you notice about their melting points?

3 **a** To what group do elements number 3, 11 and 19 belong?
b Are these elements metals or non-metals?
c Plot a graph of the melting points of these elements. What happens as the proton number goes up?
d These three elements get more reactive as the proton number increases. The next element in this group is rubidium (Rb, $Z = 39$). Predict its melting point and suggest how reactive it will be.

4 Sodium reacts with water:

sodium + water $\longrightarrow$ sodium hydroxide + hydrogen

a What would happen if you put pH paper in the water after this reaction? Why?
b What is the name given to Group I? Why do you think it is called this?

Lithium fizzes steadily in water
c What gas is given off?
d What is the name of the alkali that forms during this reaction?

5 Chlorine reacts explosively with hydrogen in sunlight to form hydrogen chloride. This gas is very soluble in water.

a What would happen if you put pH paper in a solution of hydrogen chloride in water?
b What name is given to this acid?
c What compound would form from bromine and hydrogen?
d Would you expect this reaction to be faster or slower than that with chlorine? Explain your answer.

6 **a** What name is given to the block of metals that wedge in between calcium (20) and gallium (31)? (Clue: unscramble *nottiransi*.)
b Normally the properties of the elements change dramatically as you move along the same period. What is unusual about this block of metals?
c Iron is a hard, magnetic metal with a high melting point, which forms coloured compounds. Nickel is a hard, magnetic metal with a high melting point, which forms coloured compounds. Predict the properties of cobalt (Co).

7 Element Q is a colourless gas that boils at -108 °C. It is very unreactive.

a To which group does Q belong?
b How many electrons must Q have in its outer shell?
c Is the gas made of individual atoms or molecules?

11 Metal families

1 Copy and complete the following sentences. Use the words below to fill the gaps.

electricity shiny soft alkali low reactive

The metals of Group I in the Periodic Table are called the _____ metals. They are a family of very _____ metals. They tarnish rapidly in air, but are _____ when fresh. They conduct heat and _____ well but are _____ , have low densities and _____ melting and boiling points.

2 Copy and complete the following sentences. Use the words below to fill the gaps.

melting transition harder less higher heat

The _____ metals are a family of 'everyday' metals. They are shiny and they conduct _____ and electricity. They are _____ reactive than the alkali metals, but are _____ and have higher _____ and boiling points and _____ densities.

3 Copy and complete the following sentences. Use the names below to fill the gaps.

iron (Fe) nickel (Ni) zinc (Zn)

a Steel is a form of _____ that is very strong and is used for building bridges, cars and other machinery.
b Copper is alloyed with _____ to make brass and with _____ to make coins.
c Transition metals are often used as catalysts to speed up reactions. _____ is used to make ammonia for fertilisers.

4 Copy and complete this table, using the phrases from the list at the top of the next column.

Property	Alkali metals	Transition metals
reactivity	a	b
density	c	d
mp and bp	e	f
colour of salts	g	h

very reactive   less reactive   sink in water can float on water   high   low   colourless often coloured

5 Lithium (Li), sodium (Na) and potassium (K) are the first three alkali metals, in order down the group.

a The balanced symbol equation for burning lithium in air is:
- $4Li(s) + O_2(g) \longrightarrow 2Li_2O(s)$
Write this out as a word equation.
b The alkali metals get more reactive down the group. Copy and complete this table, using the phrases from the list below.

Metal	Reaction with water	Reactivity
lithium	i	least
sodium	ii	
potassium	iii	most

- **melts, whizzes around and the gas catches fire** • **fizzes steadily**
- **melts and whizzes around**

6 The word and balanced symbol equations for sodium reacting with water are:

- sodium + water $\longrightarrow$ sodium hydroxide + hydrogen
- $2Na(s) + 2H_2O(l) \longrightarrow 2NaOH(aq) + H_2(g)$

Use these equations to help you write out the word and balanced symbol equations for potassium (K) reacting with water.

7 Rearrange these sentences to explain why the alkali metals are more reactive down the group. Copy them out in the correct order.

- The further from the nucleus, the weaker the force holding the electron in place.
- Alkali metals lose their outer electron to form positive ions when they react.
- The bigger the atom, the further the outer electron is from the positive nucleus.
- The weaker the force, the 'looser' the outer electron.
- Atoms with 'looser' outer electrons are more reactive.
- The atoms get bigger down the group.

12 Non-metal families

1 Copy and complete the following sentences. Use the words below to fill the gaps.

unreactive   reactive   atoms   molecules ionic

Group VII of the Periodic Table contains a family of very .... non-metals called the halogens. They form diatomic .... and have coloured vapours. They form .... compounds with metals.

Group VIII contains the .... noble gases. These colourless gases are made from single .... only.

2 Copy and complete this table, using the words and symbols from the list below. One line in the table has been completed for you.

| The properties of halogens... | | | |
Element	Symbol	State	Colour
fluorine	F	gas	yellow/green
chlorine			
bromine			
iodine			

Br   Cl   I   liquid   gas   solid   green purple   brown

3 Copy and complete the following sentences. Use the names of the halogens below to fill the gaps.

fluorine (F)   chlorine (Cl)   bromine (Br) iodine (I)

a The dark, almost black, crystals of .... give off a purple vapour which is used to make fingerprints show up on paper.

b .... was used as a poison gas in World War I, but is now used to kill germs in swimming baths.

c The only two elements which are liquid at room temperature are mercury and ....

d Compounds of .... such as sodium fluoride are sometimes added to drinking water as they help to strengthen teeth.

e A brown solution of .... in alcohol used to be used as an antiseptic for cuts and grazes.

4 The diagrams show how chlorine combines by covalent bonding with carbon, and by ionic bonding with sodium. Use these diagrams to draw similar diagrams and write similar equations for the reaction between bromine and carbon and between bromine and sodium.

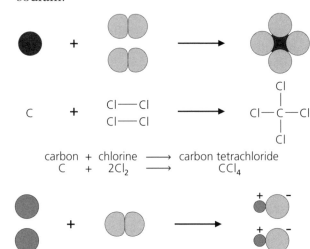

carbon + chlorine ⟶ carbon tetrachloride
  C   +   2Cl₂   ⟶   CCl₄

sodium + chlorine ⟶ sodium chloride
  2Na   +   Cl₂   ⟶   2NaCl

5 Rearrange these sentences to explain why the halogens become more reactive up the group. Copy the sentences out in the correct order.

• The closer to the nucleus, the stronger the force that might be able to capture a 'spare' electron.
• The smaller the atom, the closer any 'spare' electrons can get to the positive nucleus.
• Smaller atoms towards the top of the group will find it easier to capture an electron, and so are more reactive.
• Halogens have to gain an outer electron to form negative ions when they react.
• The atoms get smaller up the group.

1 Copy and complete the following sentences. Use the words below to fill the gaps.

harmless poisonous salt ionic chlorine sodium

.... is a dangerously reactive metal that has to be stored under oil. .... is a dangerously reactive and .... gas. They react violently together to form the .... compound, sodium chloride. Yet sodium chloride is a .... crystalline solid, known as common ....

2 Three important industrial chemicals can be made by electrolysing brine (sodium chloride solution).

Copy this diagram of the electrolysis of brine.

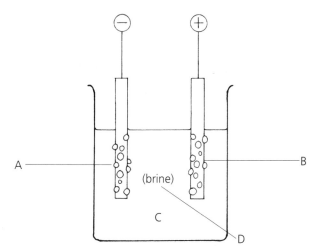

a Use the labels below in place of the letters A–D on your diagram.
  • Positive sodium and hydrogen ions are attracted to the negative electrode – hydrogen gas forms.
  • Negative chlorine ions are attracted to the positive electrode – chlorine gas is formed.
  • Sodium chloride ionises when it dissolves in water.
  • Sodium hydroxide is left in solution.
b The balanced equation for this reaction is:
  $2NaCl + 2H_2O \longrightarrow Cl_2 + H_2 + 2NaOH$
  Write this out as a word equation.
c What provides the energy needed to tear sodium chloride apart in this way?

d Here are some tests for the three products of this reaction. Copy them out, filling in the missing names.
  • A tube of .... gas will 'pop' when a flame is held up to it.
  • Damp pH paper will turn red at first in .... , but will then be bleached white.
  • A solution of .... is strongly alkaline, and will turn pH paper dark purple.
e Draw up a table to show the uses of hydrogen, chlorine and sodium hydroxide. Choose uses from:
  • Making ammonia for fertilisers
  • Making soap • Killing germs in water
  • Making paper and ceramics
  • Making plastics such as PVC
  • Making bleach (can be used twice!)
  • Making disinfectants • Cleaning ovens
  • Turning oil to fat for chocolate

3 Compounds of silver and halogens, silver halides, are used in black and white photography. For example, silver bromide breaks down when exposed to light:

$$2AgBr \xrightarrow{\text{Light}} 2Ag + Br_2$$

a Write this reaction out as a word equation.
b Rearrange these sentences to explain how the process works. Copy the sentences out in the correct order.
  • Where light falls, the compound breaks up and black grains of silver are formed.
  • In a camera, light falls on to the film for a short time.
  • This produces a negative image (black for white).
  • Where no light falls, the film stays clear.
  • Photographic film contains colourless silver bromide.

4 Hydrogen chloride forms when hydrogen gas burns in chlorine:

$$H_2 + Cl_2 \longrightarrow 2HCl$$

a Write this out as a word equation.
b When hydrogen chloride dissolves in water the solution turns pH paper red. What does this tell you?

111

14 Chemistry by numbers

1 Look at this diagram.

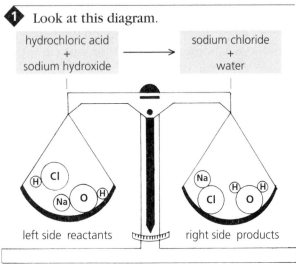

hydrochloric acid + sodium hydroxide $\longrightarrow$ sodium chloride + water

left side reactants

right side products

a balanced equation

a Write this out as a balanced chemical equation.

b Copy and complete the following sentence, which states a fundamental rule of chemistry. Choose the correct word from each group of three words in **bold**.
The **colour / mass / volume** of the reactants is equal to the **colour / mass / volume** of the products.

c Draw a diagram similar to the one above for the reaction when copper carbonate breaks down on heating.
$CuCO_3(s) \longrightarrow CuO(s) + CO_2(g)$

d Write this reaction out as a word equation.

e 12.4 g of copper carbonate was heated. When it was reweighed, its mass was only 8 g. How does this fit the rule in part **b**?

f What mass of carbon dioxide must have been formed?

2 Copy and complete the following equations, adding the missing mass values (in g).

a magnesium + oxygen $\longrightarrow$ magnesium oxide
(2.4 g)   (1.6 g)   (.........g)

b silver bromide $\longrightarrow$ silver + bromine
(1.88 g)   (1.08 g)   (.........g)

c sodium + chlorine $\longrightarrow$ sodium chloride
(.........g)   (7.1 g)   (11.7 g)

3 For each pair below, write out equation **i** as a word equation and write a balanced equation for reaction **ii**.

a i $2Na + Br_2 \longrightarrow 2NaBr$
ii sodium reacts with chlorine (Cl) to give sodium chloride

b i $2Mg + O_2 \longrightarrow 2MgO$
ii calcium (Ca) burns in oxygen to give calcium oxide

c i $4Na + O_2 \longrightarrow 2Na_2O$
ii potassium (K) burns in oxygen to give potassium oxide

4 Here are some unbalanced equations.
i Write out each reaction as a word equation.
ii Balance each chemical equation.

a $CaO + HCl \longrightarrow CaCl_2 + H_2O$
b $K + H_2O \longrightarrow KOH + H_2$
c $CaCO_3 + HCl \longrightarrow CaCl_2 + H_2O + CO_2$
d $Mg + HCl \longrightarrow MgCl_2 + H_2$

5 Atoms gain or lose electrons when they form ions. For example, an aluminium atom loses three electrons to form an Al^{3+} ion. This can be written as $Al \longrightarrow Al^{3+} + 3e^-$ (electrons). Write similar ionic equations for the following changes.

a A sodium (Na) atom becoming an Na^+ ion.
b A copper (Cu) atom becoming a Cu^{2+} ion.
c A chlorine *atom* becoming a Cl^- ion.
d A chlorine *molecule* (Cl_2) becoming *two* Cl^- ions.

6 Electrolysis is like ionisation in reverse. So, in the electrolysis of molten aluminium oxide, the change at the negative electrode is
$Al^{3+} + 3e^- \longrightarrow Al$

a What happens to an oxygen *ion* at the positive electrode in this reaction?
b Oxygen *molecules* (O_2), not separate atoms, are given off at the positive electrode. Write this as a simple equation.
c What happens at the positive and negative electrodes when molten salt (NaCl) is electrolysed? (See **Q5a** and **Q5d**.)

1 Copy and complete the following sentences. Use the words below to fill the gaps.

electrical light kinetic energy sound

There are many forms of .... The Sun sends out .... and heat energy. Loudspeakers give out .... energy. A moving car has .... energy. Batteries or 'the mains' provide .... energy.

2 Look at this picture. Make a list of all the different forms of energy you can see in it.

3 Some forms of energy are *active* – you can see something happening – while some forms of energy are *stored* and need to be 'released' in some way.

Copy and complete this table, using the types of energy from the list below.

Active energy	Stored energy

- **chemical energy**
- **potential energy**
- **electrical energy**
- **light energy**
- **kinetic energy**
- **heat energy**

4 Stored energy can be turned into active energy. Copy and complete the following sentences. Choose the correct form of energy from each of the pairs given.

a Natural gas contains stored **chemical / elastic** energy. This turns into **heat / electrical** energy when it burns.

b A clockwork motor contains stored **chemical / mechanical** energy. It turns into **light / kinetic** energy when the spring unwinds.

c A battery contains stored **chemical / mechanical** energy. It turns into **electrical / kinetic** energy when the wires are connected.

d Petrol contains stored **chemical / mechanical** energy. It turns into **light / kinetic** energy when it explodes in the engine and makes the car move.

e A stretched bow contains stored **chemical / mechanical** energy. It turns into **heat / kinetic** energy when the bow is released.

5 Many common devices turn one form of energy into another. Copy and complete the following sentences. Choose the correct word from each of the pairs given. For each part of this question you should be able to do this in two different ways, to make *two* correct sentences.

a A **microphone / loudspeaker** turns **electrical / sound** energy into **electrical / sound** energy.

b An electric **motor / generator** turns **electrical / kinetic** energy into **electrical / kinetic** energy.

c A **solar cell / light bulb** turns **electrical / light** energy into **electrical / light** energy.

d A roller-coaster free-rolling **up / down** turns **potential / kinetic** energy into **potential / kinetic** energy.

1 Copy and complete the following sentences. Use the words below to fill the gaps.

**convection   poor   radiation   currents
conductors**

Metals are good .... of heat energy. The heat energy is passed along the solid. Liquids and gases are .... conductors but, if heated from below, moving .... are set up which move the heat energy by ....

Hot things also give out heat energy as 'heat rays' – .... This is the only way that heat energy can pass through empty space. It is how we get energy from the Sun.

2 Poor conductors are called insulators.

Copy and complete this table, using the materials from the list below.

Conductors	Insulators

**copper   wood   aluminium   ice   silver
plastic   glass   brass**

3 Explain the following situations.

a Frying pans are made of metal, but the handles are made of plastic or wood.

b Stainless steel cups are not very good for drinking hot drinks from.

c Hot serving dishes are sometimes put onto a cork mat rather than straight onto a polished table.

4 Copy the following diagram. Use the labels below in place of the letters A–D on your diagram, to explain how water is heated by convection.

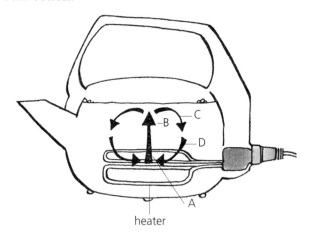

heater

- The water cools and contracts.
- The water is heated and expands.
- It sinks back down, passing back over the heater.
- The hot water floats up through the cooler water.

5 Look at this graph, which shows the temperature of a cup of coffee as it cools down.

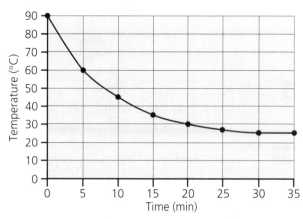

a What was the temperature after 5 minutes?
b How much did the temperature drop in the *first* 5 minutes?
c How much did the temperature drop in the *second* 5 minutes?
d Why was there a bigger temperature drop in the first 5 minutes than in the second 5 minutes?
e What do you think the temperature would be after 40 minutes? Why?

1 Copy and complete the following sentences. Use the words below to fill the gaps.

bubbles   energy   trapped   radiation
insulators   fibres

Wasted heat .... wastes money. We use .... to help stop heat energy escaping. Air is a good insulator if it is .... so that it cannot move. Air can be trapped in .... in expanded polystyrene, or between the .... of a woolly jumper. Shiny silver surfaces help to reduce heat loss by ....

2 Copy this diagram of a vacuum flask. Use the labels below in place of the letters A–D on your diagram.

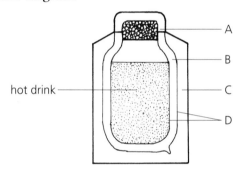

- Vacuum to stop heat loss by conduction and convection.
- Hollow, double-layered glass bottle, with silvered surfaces to reduce heat loss by radiation.
- Hard case to protect the glass.
- Plastic or cork lid to stop heat loss by conduction through the top.

3 Terry and Seehra set up an experiment like this.

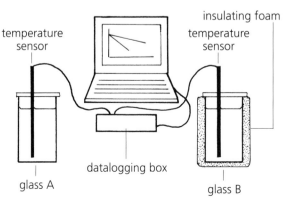

They put boiling water into the two glasses and started the datalogging program. Here is the graph that the computer produced.

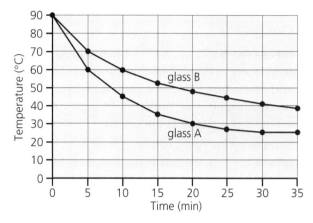

a What was the water temperature in glass A after 10 minutes?

b What was the water temperature in glass B after 10 minutes?

c Why is the water temperature in glass B higher than that in glass A?

d What is the difference in temperature after 35 minutes?

e What do you think the difference in temperature would be after 1 hour? Explain your answer.

4 Julie and Anton performed an experiment similar to that in **Q3** using two metal cans without insulation.

a Use their results to plot a graph showing how the temperature dropped in the two cans.

Time (mins)	Can A (°C)	Can B (°C)
0	90	90
5	60	70
10	43	58
15	33	50
20	27	44
25	25	39
30	25	35

b One of their cans had a shiny silver surface, while the other had been painted matt black. Which can was which? Explain your answer.

1 Copy and complete the following sentences. Use the words below to fill the gaps.

expensive fossil heating continuous

Nearly 90% of the energy used in the average home goes on _____ and hot water. This energy may be obtained by burning _____ fuels – coal, oil or gas. Gas is most commonly used as a _____ supply may be piped in. Electricity is also used. This is very convenient but is generally more _____ .

2 This pie chart shows how heat is lost from a typical home.

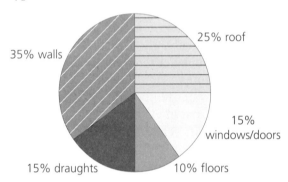

35% walls
25% roof
15% windows/doors
10% floors
15% draughts

a Which part of the house loses the most heat?
b More heat is lost through 1m² of window than 1m² of wall. Explain why window heat loss is less important overall.
c A house costs £500 a year to heat. How much of this money is 'wasted' due to draughts? (Assume that all of the energy lost in this way may be saved.)
d A firm gives an estimate of £150 to fit draught excluders. How long would it take for the savings on heat loss to 'pay' for this expenditure?
e The owner decides to fit the draught excluders herself. She has worked out that she will get her money back in 8 months. How much must the draught excluders cost to buy?
f The owner knows that double glazing would reduce energy loss through the windows by a half, but she is quoted £2250 to do the job. Do you think this would be a good idea, in terms of potential energy savings? Explain your answer.

3 Cavity walls can be filled with insulating material to reduce heat loss. There are several different types of filler used. They are 'rated' for different properties in the chart below on a 1 to 5 scale (5 = good, 4 = quite good, 3 = reasonable, 2 = not very good, 1 = poor).

The categories in the table are:
• **Env**: environmental impact – good means no problem.
• **Health**: associated health problems – good means no problem.
• **Energy**: how good is it for saving energy?
• **Use**: is it easy / reliable to use?

Material	Env	Health	Energy	Use
fibreglass	4	2	4	5
mineral wool	5	3	4	5
cellulose	5	4	5	4
polystyrene	3	4	4	4
polyurethane	3	3	5	4
vermiculite	4	3	3	4

a Copy this table, add an extra column for 'total score' and fill in this extra column.
b Which material gets the best score overall?
c Draw a bar chart for the total score value of these materials.
d Cellulose filler is made from recycled paper. Do you think its environment score would be so high if it were not recycled? Explain your answer.
e Polystyrene and polyurethane are made from oil. Which low values does this explain? Explain your answer.
f Polystyrene can be recycled. How would this affect its 'total score' as an insulator?
g Some old houses were built with hollow cavity walls. Today, insulation is fitted as the walls are built. Most insulation comes as blocks or sheets, but polyurethane foam is squirted in as a liquid, which then bubbles, swells and sets. Explain why polyurethane foam is sometimes used to insulate the empty cavities in these older houses, despite its 'lower' total score on the chart above.

1 Copy the three diagrams. Write the correct caption under each diagram, choosing the correct word from those shown in bold.

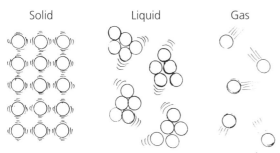

Solid   Liquid   Gas

A In a **liquid** / **solid** / **gas**, the particles are close together, but are free to move about.
B In a **liquid** / **solid** / **gas**, the particles are close together and are held in place, but they can still vibrate.
C In a **liquid** / **solid** / **gas**, the particles are far apart and are moving at high speed.

2 **a** Rearrange these sentences to explain how heat energy is conducted along a metal rod. Copy the sentences out in the correct order.

- In this way, the energy is spread out through the metal, away from the source.
- When a metal is heated, these electrons are given more energy and so speed up.
- In metals, some of these electrons are loose and are free to move around.
- These faster electrons spread out through the metal.
- Atoms have tiny charged particles called electrons whizzing around them.
- The electrons collide with other particles, and some of their energy is transferred.

b Draw a simple diagram to show this effect in action.

3 Explain why a hot air balloon rises. You will need to include:

- What happens to the gas particles when they are heated.
- What this does to the volume of gas.
- What this does to the density of the gas.
- What effect altering the density of the gas has.

4 Copy this diagram of a radiator in a room. Label your diagram, using a similar series of ideas to those in **Q3** for the first part of your explanation.

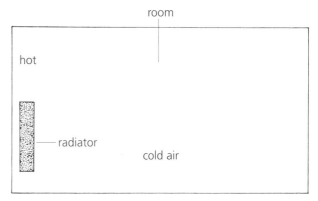

5 **a** The heat energy from the Sun reaches us by radiation. How do you know that it does not reach us by conduction or convection?
b What form does this heat radiation take?
c In hot and sunny countries, such as Greece, houses are often painted white. What advantage does this have?
d The water pipes in solar panels are painted matt black. Explain why.
e Chinese take-away meals are often served in shiny aluminium containers. Aluminium is a very good conductor, so why do these meals stay hot for a long while?

6 Use your understanding of conduction, convection and radiation to explain the following:

a Peter's bedroom is in the attic of his house. The room has a very large, south-facing window set into the roof which cannot be opened. The room gets very hot and stuffy in the summer.
b Jacqui had a fall on a mountainside and couldn't move. She was trapped out in the open on a cold night. She survived by lying on a pile of dry grass and wrapping herself in a silver 'space blanket'.
c Rescuers searched all night for Jacqui using a thermal imaging camera, which picks up body heat radiation. The rescuers failed to find Jacqui. Why was that?

1 Copy and complete the following sentences. Use the words below to fill the gaps.

energy   watts   joules

Energy is measured in .... Power is a measure of how fast .... is transferred. Power is measured in ....

2 Look at the meter readings shown:

37526   38776

1st January 1998   1st April 1998

a How many units of electricity were used that 'quarter'?
b If every unit of electricity cost 8p, what would 1000 units cost?
c What would 250 units cost?
d What was the bill for the quarter shown?

3
$$\text{power (watts)} = \frac{\text{energy (joules)}}{\text{time (seconds)}}$$

Use this equation to work out the power rating of the following

a a light bulb that transfers 600 J of energy in 10 seconds
b A vacuum cleaner motor that transfers 1200 J in 2 seconds
c a toaster that transfers 1000 J in 4 seconds
d a radio that transfers 60 J in 1 minute (careful!)
e an electric fire that transfers 1500 J in half a second
f an electric toothbrush that transfers 5 J in 50 seconds.

4   energy transferred (J) = power (W) x time (s)

Use this equation to work out the energy transferred when

a a 250 W food mixer is on for 5 seconds
b a 1 W radio is left on for 1 hour
c a 500 W vacuum cleaner is used for 5 minutes
d a 100 W TV is on for 2 hours
e a 2 kW fire is on for 1 minute
f a 5 W 'night light' is left on for 10 hours.

5 The 'unit' of electricity is the kilowatt hour (kWh). This is the amount of electricity used by a 1 kW fire in 1 hour. You can calculate it using the formula:

$$\text{kWh} = \frac{\text{power (W)} \times \text{time used (hours)}}{1000}$$

Copy and complete the table below, which works out the daily running costs of some different electrical appliances. Assume that 1 kWh costs 8p.

Appliance	Wattage (W)	Time used (hours)	No of kWh	Cost (£)
light bulb	100	10	a	b
TV	100	5	c	d
electric fire	3000	3	e	f
freezer	250	2	g	h
kettle	2000	0.1	i	j

6 Electric fires are very efficient, as 99% of the electrical energy is turned into useful heat energy. Petrol engines are far less efficient, as only about 35% of the stored chemical energy is turned into useful kinetic energy. Of the rest, 5% is released as sound and the rest is 'wasted' as heat energy.

a Draw pie charts to show the percentage energy conversions in electric fires and petrol engines.
b For each of the following electrical devices, suggest what has happened to the 'missing' energy:
  • light bulb: electricity ⟶ 8% light + ...
  • food mixer: electricity ⟶ 50% kinetic energy + ...
  • transformer: mains electricity ⟶ 90% 12V electricity + ...
  • vacuum cleaner: electricity ⟶ 70% kinetic energy + ...
c i Arrange the energy changes from part **b** in order of increasing efficiency.
  ii Display this information as an efficiency bar chart.

8 *Energy change efficiency*

 Copy and complete the following definitions. Choose the correct word from each of the pairs given.

The **weight / mass** of an object (in newtons) is the force that acts on it due to the pull of **electricity / gravity**. The weight of 1 kg of water on Earth is approximately 10 newtons (10 N).

 The change in gravitational potential energy is given by the formula:

change in gravitational potential energy (J)
   = weight (N) x change in vertical height (m)

Calculate the change in gravitational potential energy in each of the following cases.

a Jack weighs 400 N. He falls 10 m vertically down a hill.
b A 25 N cat is hoisted 20 m out of a well.
c A volcano blasts a 100 N block of lava 300 m into the air.
d A 1 N spanner falls 200 m from a skyscraper.

3 Copy the following formula:

energy (J) = power (W) x time (s)

Use this formula to calculate the energy used if

a a 50 W motor runs for 20 seconds
b a 100 W motor runs for 1 minute
c a 10 W motor runs for 1 hour.

4 Copy the following formula:

efficiency = $\dfrac{\text{useful energy output (J)}}{\text{total energy input (J)}}$ x 100%

Use this formula to calculate the efficiency of the following devices. Show your working.

a It takes 500 J of energy to push a box up a ramp (total energy input). However, the box only gains 300 J of potential energy (useful energy output).
b It only takes 400 J to *roll* a barrel up the same ramp, giving the same gain in potential energy (300 J).
c It takes a total energy input of 750 J to lift a 600 N bucket of water by 1 m (a useful energy output of 600 J) using a pulley.

5 Screw-thread car jacks were used to lift a 10 000 N car by 10 cm.

a What was the change in potential energy?
b The total amount of energy used to crank up the jacks was 20 000 J. What was the efficiency?
c Ordinary car jacks like this are not very efficient. This is because they have to overcome a lot of friction in the screw-thread. What form of energy do you think the 'wasted' part has turned into?
d Hydraulic car jacks are more efficient. A hydraulic jack lifted the same car to the same height. Its 35 W electric motor had to run for 40 seconds to do this. How much energy did the motor 'use' to do this?
e Calculate the efficiency of this hydraulic jack.

6 **a** A conventional, coal-fired power station 'loses' 9% of its energy when the fuel is first burnt. For every 1 MJ of stored chemical energy in the coal, how much is 'lost' at this stage? How much remains?
b Gas-fired power stations are more efficient at this stage, losing only 5%. How much energy is 'kept' in this case from every 1 MJ?
c Of this retained energy from part **b**, 53% is lost as waste heat in the cooling towers. How much energy (in kJ) remains after this stage?
d If another 46 kJ is lost in the generator plant, how much electrical energy is produced?
e Heat exchangers can be used to trap some of the 'waste' heat energy and use it to heat water for greenhouses or homes. If the heat exchangers are 90% efficient, how much additional energy could be 'saved' from the original 1 MJ in a gas-fired power station, using your figures from part **c**?

1 Copy and complete the following sentences. Use the words below to fill the gaps.

renewable   fuels   replace   fossil

We get a lot of the energy we need by burning .... such as coal, oil, gas and wood. Wood is a .... fuel as we can always grow more trees. Coal, oil and gas are .... fuels that take millions of years to form. Once the fossil fuels have all been burnt, we cannot .... them. They are non-renewable.

2 Look at the pie chart, which shows the use of different fuels worldwide in 1995.

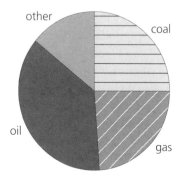

Roughly what proportion of the world's energy comes from

a coal?   (choose from ¼ ½ ¾)
b gas?   (choose from ¼ ½ ¾)
c Which fuel is used the most?

3 This chart shows when fossil fuels will run out.

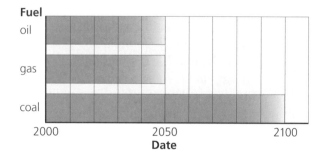

a Which fossil fuel will still be available in 2075?
b Why will it be a problem in 2075 that there is no oil or gas? (Look back at **Q2**.)
c What effect will 'save it' campaigns have on the date when oil and gas run out?
d How will this help?

4 Wood is a renewable fuel as new wood can always be grown. Copy the diagram. Use the labels below in place of the letters A–D on your diagram.

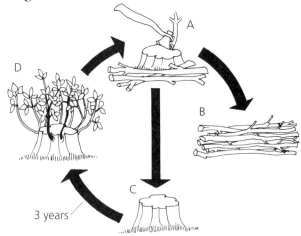

- The stump is left in place.
- The tree is cut down just above the roots.
- New branches grow on the stump.
- The branches are used as fuel wood.

5 Look at the diagram of a power station. Which of the labels below could be used to replace the letters A–E? Copy the labels out in the correct order, to explain how the power station works.

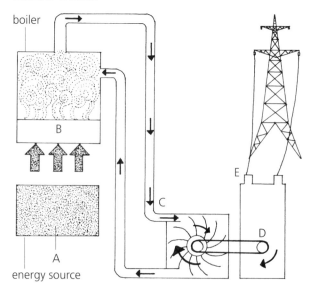

- The generator produces electricity.
- Expanding steam turns the turbine.
- The fuel is burnt to give heat energy.
- The turbine spins the generator.
- This boils the water.

1 Copy and complete the following sentences. Use the words below to fill the gaps.

hydroelectric potential kinetic turbines

Water high in the mountains has lots of gravitational.................. energy. This turns to .... energy as the water flows downhill. The energy in flowing water can be used to turn .... and generate electricity. This happens in.................. power stations.

2 The amount of electrical power used in any part of the country varies with the time of day.

Plot a graph of the power usage in one region using the following data:

Time (24hr clock)	Power used (GW) (1 GW = 1000 MW)
00.00/24.00	5
06.00	5
09.00	8
10.00	7
18.00	7
19.00	9
22.00	8

3 Hydroelectric power plants can be switched on or off in minutes, but conventional fossil fuel stations have to be kept running all the time. If they are shut down, they take days to start up again.

The region described in **Q2** has six 1 GW fossil fuel power stations, two 1 GW hydroelectric power stations and is connected to the National Grid. Use this information and the 'power used' table from **Q2** to answer the following questions.

a The six fossil fuel stations are kept on all night. Why not shut one down to save energy?
b How is the demand for power at 09.00 hrs met?
c What do you think happens at 10.00 hrs?
d At what time does the region have to buy in extra electricity from the National Grid?

4 Nadbridge is a beautiful town set in lovely countryside at the head of the Nad valley, next to water meadows fed by annual river floods. The town is growing and there is a new estate by the river. As a result, the town now needs more electricity. However, the new estate was badly flooded after heavy rain, when the river burst its banks. The council has decided to overcome both of these problems by damming the river (from A to B) to stop it flooding and to generate electricity. A new lake will form behind the dam, up to the 30 m contour on the map.

a Environmentalists are opposing the plan. List as many reasons as you can think of (from the information given) why they might not like the plan.

The council says that, without this scheme, they will need to build a new gas-fired power station outside the town. This would be unsightly, and would give off greenhouse gases (carbon dioxide) and other pollutants that would harm the environment. They would also need to spend millions of pounds on river defences. A new dam and its lake would be good for wildlife, they say, and would be a useful leisure facility.

b Make a list of arguments for and against the plan.

121

1 Copy and complete the following sentences. Use the words below to fill the gaps.

Sun   water   cells   panels   expensive

The .... provides us with an almost limitless supply of 'free' energy. Solar .... turn sunlight directly into electricity, but they are .... Solar .... produce hot .... for cleaning or heating, and are much cheaper to make.

2 Look at the diagram of a solar panel. Which of the labels below could be used to replace the letters A–E? Copy the labels out in the correct order, to explain how the solar panel works.

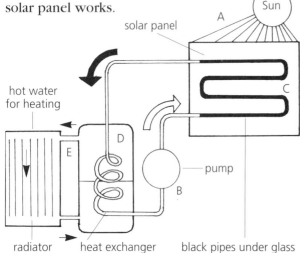

- The heated water passes through a heat exchanger.
- The water in the pipes is heated.
- Cold water is pumped into the solar panel.
- Hot water is produced for heating.
- Sunlight shines on the solar panel.

3 Solar cells are reliable and relatively cheap to make for low-power devices, but high-powered versions are very expensive. Would they be suitable for the following uses? Explain your answer in each case.

a A calculator.   b An electric car.
c A 'top-up' battery charger for a car.
d Home heating.
e Powering an earthquake sensor left on a volcano.
f Powering a telecommunications satellite.

4 John and Judy own the same type of house, but Judy has had a solar panel installed in her roof to provide hot water and some heating. Here are their costs for heating and hot water.

| | Quarterly costs (£)... | |
	John	Judy
summer hot water	6	0
autumn hot water	10	4
winter hot water	16	12
spring hot water	12	4
summer heating	20	0
autumn heating	40	17
winter heating	60	50
spring heating	40	17

a Draw separate bar charts of John's and Judy's hot water and heating costs over the four seasons.
b Draw a bar chart to compare John,s and Judy's combined costs over the four seasons.
c In what season did Judy make the greatest saving? How much was this saving?
d In what season did she make the least saving? How much was this saving?
e Explain why you think the season in part **d** gave the least savings?
f Why doesn't summer give the greatest saving?
g Calculate Judy's total saving over the year.
h If she paid £500 for the solar panel, how many years would it take her to 'get her money back'?
i Why might solar panels like this be a good idea apart from the financial savings?

5 Energy from sunlight can amount to as much as 1 kW per square metre.

a How much energy would fall onto a square kilometre at this rate? (1 km² = 1000 m x 1000 m)
b In practice, the *average* value will be much less, perhaps just 10% of the maximum value. List some possible reasons for this.
c Calculate the *average* power falling on 1 km².
d Solar cells are only 25% efficient. What power output would you get from 1 km² of these?

1 Copy and complete the following sentences. Use the words below to fill the gaps.

air generators Sun

Energy from the .... drives the world's weather systems. The power of moving .... has been harnessed for centuries by windmills. Modern windmills turn .... and produce electricity.

2 A modern wind generator can produce just over 300 kW of electrical power, so you need three to produce 1 MW.

a How many wind generators would you need to replace a 1 GW (1000 MW) power station?
b You can only put 5 wind generators on a square kilometre (1 km²) of land. How many square kilometres of land would you need to replace a 1 GW power station with wind generators?
c Juralay is a very windy island. It has a big port that needs its own 1 GW coal-fired power station to meet its needs.

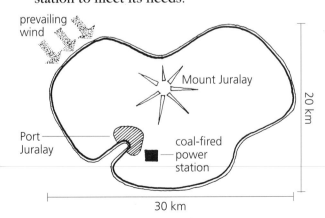

Some Juralay residents think the power station is ugly and want to replace it with a wind farm. Is their idea a good one? Explain your answer.

3 Look at the map of Scotland, showing the *average* annual wind speed in metres per second.

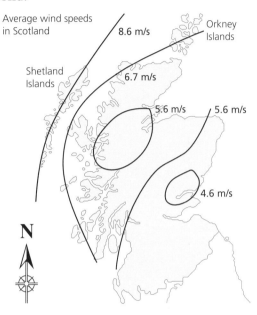

a The stronger the wind, the more power it can generate. Where would be the best place to build wind generators, based on this simple idea alone?
b If the wind is too strong, 9 or 10 m/s for example, the generators have to be shut down to avoid damage. Can you see a possible problem for your answer to part **a**, given this new information?
c The isolated Orkney Islands have a small population. All the power they need is generated by a very large wind generator. Suggest some reasons why this is a better solution to their power needs than a power station burning fossil fuels.

4 Rearrange these sentences to explain how wave-powered generators work. Copy the sentences out in the correct order.
• The water moves up and then down as a wavefront passes.
• The turbine spins a generator, which produces electricity.
• The compressed air is forced through pipes, where it turns a turbine.
• As the water rises, the air is compressed.
• The advancing wave is made to trap air under a concrete dome.

1 Copy and complete the following sentences. Use the words below to fill the gaps.

turbines   day   water   Moon

Twice a .... , the sea level around the coast of Britain rises and falls by several meters, due to the gravitational pull of the .... As the tides come in and out, the energy in the moving .... can be used to spin .... and drive electrical generators.

2 In France, a barrage across the Rance estuary generates 250 MW of electricity.

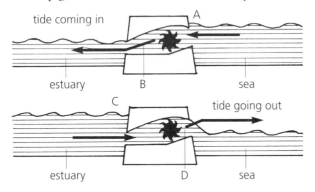

Look at the diagram of the Rance barrage. Which of the labels below could be used to replace the letters A–D? Copy the labels out in the correct order, to explain how the Rance barrage works.

- This flows out through the turbines, spinning them again to produce electricity.
- The turbines spin generators and produce electricity.
- As the tide goes out, water is trapped behind the barrage.
- As the tide comes in, water is forced through the turbines.

3 A barrage could be built across the Severn estuary, between England and Wales. It would be nearly 20 km long with over 200 turbines, each capable of producing 40 MW.

a How far apart would the turbines be on average?
b What would the total power output be?
c If a typical power station has a 1 GW output, how many would this barrage be equivalent to?

d The projected cost for this scheme is £8000 million. A new gas-fired power station would cost about £500 million. Is the barrage worth building on simple economic grounds? Explain your answer.
e Why, in the long term, is it worth considering?

4 In Yellowstone National Park in the USA, boiling water squirts out of the ground from geysers such as 'Old Faithful'.

a What does this tell us about the rocks underground there?
b Why can't this geothermal energy be trapped directly from the geysers?
c Geothermal power stations elsewhere exploit the hot rocks beneath the surface. Copy the diagram of a geothermal power station. Use the labels below in place of the letters A–D to explain how the process works.

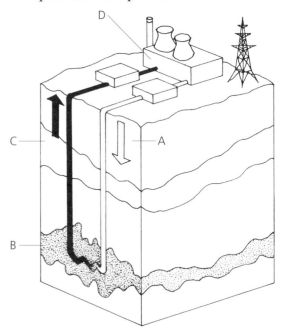

- The cold water passes through cracks in hot rock and becomes very hot.
- It turns to steam at the surface and is made to spin turbines; the turbines turn generators which produce electricity.
- Cold water is pumped down a borehole.
- The superheated water rises back up another borehole.

1 Copy and complete the following sentences. Use the words below to fill the gaps.

burnt   uranium   radioactive   decay

Nuclear power stations get their energy from nuclear fuels such as plutonium or .... These are not .... They give out energy when their atoms break down by a process called radioactive .... This gives out a lot of energy but unfortunately leaves a lot of dangerous .... waste.

2 Copy this simplified diagram of a nuclear power station. Use the labels below in place of the letters A–D on your diagram.

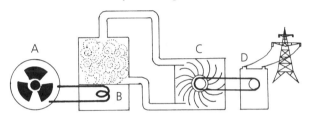

- The expanding steam spins turbines.
- The nuclear reactor produces a lot of heat energy.
- The turbines spin generators which produce electricity.
- This energy is used to boil water to make steam.

3 A nuclear reactor has the following features. Match each feature with its purpose, and then copy out the complete sentence.

a A fuel rod   .....picks up the heat energy from the reactor and carries it out.

b A thick concrete case   .....contains the uranium or plutonium fuel.

c A reactor core   .....stops the harmful radiation escaping.

d Liquid sodium in pipes   .....is where the reaction takes place with the fuel in the rods.

4 Thirty years ago, the costs of different ways of producing energy were compared by looking at:

- the initial power station construction costs;
- the running costs, which were mostly affected by fuel costs.

This graph shows the accumulating costs for two power stations. Both are producing a constant 1 GW power output.

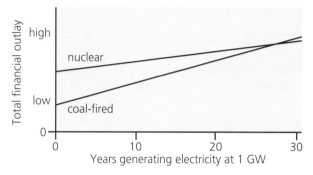

a Which type of power station has the higher construction costs?
b Which has the lower running (fuel) costs? (Clue: look at how fast the total cost rises with time.)
c Which type will have produced the most electricity per £ after 20 years?
d Which type will have produced the most electricity per £ after 30 years?
e After approximately how many years are the two types equally cost effective?

Nowadays, the cost of decommissioning the power station after its working life is also taken into account. This lifetime may be taken as 30 years. The cost of decommissioning a coal-fired power station is relatively low – much less than the construction costs. The cost of decommissioning a nuclear power station is high – about the same as zconstruction costs.
f Taking this new information into account, which method is the most cost effective for the production of electricity overall? (Which method has the lowest total costs over the life of the power station?)
g Despite this, some people argue that more nuclear power stations will be needed in the future. Suggest a reason for this.

1 The government of the developing region of Brochavna is reviewing its energy needs. The major city of Brocha is growing at an alarming rate. The old power stations cannot provide enough electricity. Within 5 years they will need a total of 4 GW of power, only half of which can be provided by the existing power stations.

The map gives existing sites and suggestions for the future. Some information is given about different methods of power generation.

Devise an energy plan to meet the needs of Brochavna in 5 years time. Give reasons for your choice, as well as reasons for not adopting the alternatives.

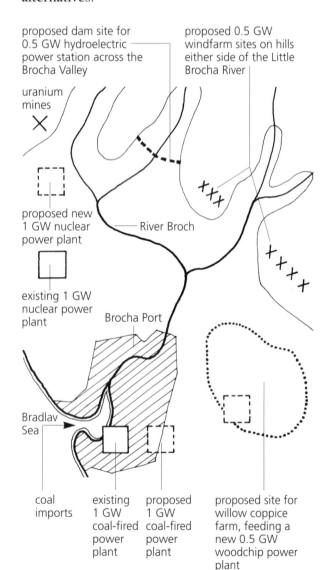

proposed dam site for 0.5 GW hydroelectric power station across the Brocha Valley

proposed 0.5 GW windfarm sites on hills either side of the Little Brocha River

uranium mines

proposed new 1 GW nuclear power plant

River Broch

existing 1 GW nuclear power plant

Brocha Port

Bradlav Sea

coal imports

existing 1 GW coal-fired power plant

proposed 1 GW coal-fired power plant

proposed site for willow coppice farm, feeding a new 0.5 GW woodchip power plant

Nuclear power generation
For
- Low fuel costs for power generation.
- Long-term nuclear fuel supplies available.
- No greenhouse gases produced.
- Reliable continuous electricity supply.

Against
- High construction costs.
- High decommissioning costs.
- Radioactive waste disposal problems.
- Danger of a Chernobyl-style accident.

Fossil fuel power generation
For
- Relatively low construction costs.
- Low decommissioning costs.
- Reliable continuous electricity supply.

Against
- Greenhouse gas emissions.
- Fuel mining/drilling or importing problems.
- Fossils fuels will run out (non-renewable).

Woodchip power generation
For
- Relatively low construction costs.
- Renewable fuel if wood is farmed.
- Reliable continuous electricity supply.

Against
- Greenhouse gas emissions.
- 'Bulkier' fuel than coal.

Hydroelectric power generation
For
- Clean, safe generation.   • No fuel costs.
- Can be switched on or off quickly.

Against
- Valleys must be dammed.
- Limited power output.

Wind generators
For
- Clean, safe generation.   • No fuel costs.
- Can be switched on or off quickly.

Against
- High capital costs as 'low grade' energy source.
- Large area needed for a large output.
- Unreliable – the wind does not always blow.

1 Copy and complete the following sentences. Use the words below to fill the gaps.

static   electrically   attract

When materials such as wool and nylon are rubbed together, they become .... charged. They can .... and pick up small pieces of paper near them. This type of electricity is called .... electricity.

2 Many effects are caused by static electricity? From the list below, copy out those effects that are caused by static electricity.

- Nylon jumpers make a crackling sound when you pull them off.
- TV screens get dusty very quickly.
- Fridge magnets stick to fridge doors.
- Balloons stick to the wall if you rub them on your jumper.
- Lightning is common during heavy storms.
- Suction caps stick to mirrors.
- You can sometimes get an electric shock from a metal object if you have just walked over a nylon carpet.
- You can get an electric shock from a bare wire on the 'mains'.

3 Rearrange these sentences to explain what causes static electricity. Copy the sentences out in the correct order.

- The one that loses some negative charges becomes positively charged overall.
- These charges usually balance out.
- If enough charges build up, they can jump back together, causing a spark.
- The one that gains extra negative charges becomes negatively charged overall.
- If you rub two substances together, negative charges may be knocked from one to the other.
- Opposite charges attract one another.
- All substances carry both positive (+) and negative (-) charges.

4 Abdul performed an experiment to see which materials produced the largest electrostatic effect. He did this by rubbing the material with a dry duster and then gradually lowering it onto some Rice Crispies, until they were attracted up to it. The larger the electrostatic effect, the higher the Rice Crispies 'jumped'. Here are his results.

Material	Height jumped (cm)
nylon comb	10
glass rod	5
cellulose acetate	8
ebonite rod	7
perspex ruler	3

a Which material showed the greatest static effect?
b Plot a bar chart of Abdul's results.

5 Copy the diagram of a simple photocopying process. Use the labels below in place of the letters A–D on your diagram.

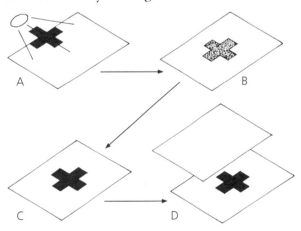

- Dry ink powder is attracted to the charge.
- The ink is transferred to paper.
- This leaves a negative image in the charge.
- Light falls on to a special charged material.

6 Hospitals use flammable chemicals such as ether that could be ignited by static sparks. A trolley with rubber wheels could get charged up enough by the movement of blankets or sheets to cause such a spark. Hospital trolleys now have a short length of chain dangling from the metal frame to the floor to stop this. How does this help?

1 Copy and complete the following sentences. Use the words below to fill the gaps.

electrons   current   insulators   conductors

Static charges can build up on .... , which do not allow the charges to move easily. Metals are not like this. They allow small negatively charged particles called .... to move through them. They are .... A flow of moving electrons is called a .... of electricity.

2 Electrons need an energy input from some kind of 'electron pump' to make them flow around a circuit. Link the following 'electron pumps' to the energy source that drives them. Copy out your answers.

'electron pump'	energy source
generator	sound
battery	light
microphone	movement (kinetic)
solar cell	chemical

3 Look at the diagram. Bulbs have a coil made of resistance wire in them.

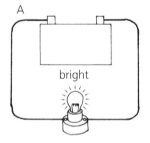
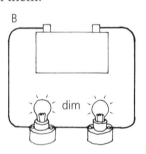

a Explain why the bulb in circuit A gets hot when electricity passes through it.
b The bulbs in circuit B are the same as in circuit A. Is more or less current flowing through circuit B than circuit A? How can you tell?
c If a third bulb was added into circuit B, would the brightness of the bulbs increase or decrease? Explain your answer.
d If a second battery was added to circuit A, would the bulb get brighter or dimmer? Explain your answer.
e What would happen if the wire in circuit A was broken?

4 Dimmer switches have a coil of resistance wire in them, and a sliding contact that can make the electricity pass through all or just part of the wire.

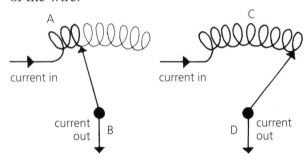

Copy the diagram of a dimmer switch. Use the labels below in place of the letters A–D on your diagram.
• This gives a low current and dim light.
• This gives a high current and bright light.
• Long wire gives high resistance.
• Short wire gives low resistance.

5 A single cell provides a potential difference of about 1.5 V. These can be stacked up to increase the voltage, but if they are connected the wrong way around, they can cancel out.

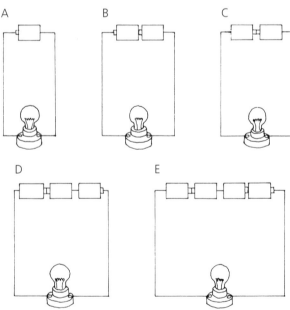

a What voltage will provided in each of the circuits A–E?
b How many of these cells would there be in a 12 V dry battery?

1 Copy and complete the following sentences. Use the words below to fill the gaps.

parallel   series

A circuit where all the components are in a single loop is called a .... circuit. If the circuit has two or more loops, it is called a .... circuit.

2 Copy these circuits and say whether they are series or parallel.

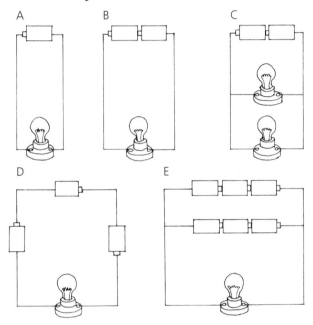

A   B   C

D   E

3 Copy the following symbols. Use the words below to explain what each symbol stands for.

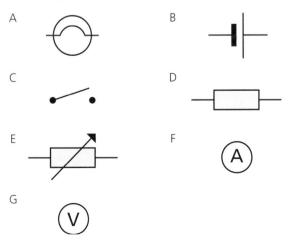

A   B

C   D

E   F

G

resistor   voltmeter   variable resistor
ammeter   switch (open)   lamp   cell

4 Describe the following simple circuits in words.

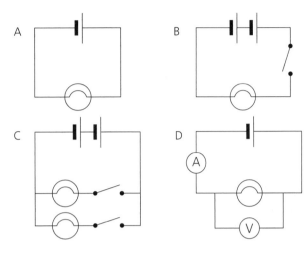

A   B

C   D

5 Draw simple circuit diagrams for each of the following

a two bulbs in a simple series circuit with two cells
b a bulb in series with one cell and a variable resistor
c an ammeter in series with a resistor and a cell; a voltmeter in parallel across the resistor
d two bulbs in parallel with a single cell; an open switch in the main loop of the circuit.

6 Which bulbs, if any, would light up in each of circuits A–D?

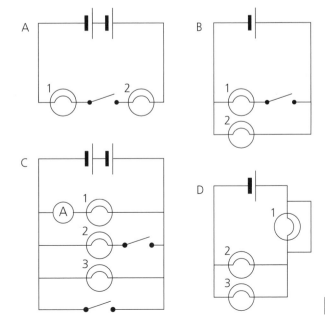

A   B

C   D

129

1 Copy and complete the following sentences. Use the words below to fill the gaps.

direct   alternating   batteries   backwards

The current always flows in the same direction in the electricity from _____ . This is called _____ current (d.c.). In mains electricity, the current direction switches _____ and forwards 50 times a second. This is called _____ current (a.c.).

2 Copy this diagram of a mains cable. Use the labels below in place of the letters A–D on your diagram.

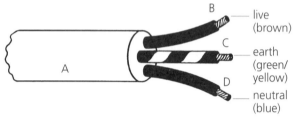

- Flexible plastic case for insulation.
- Copper wires to conduct electricity.
- Colour coded for identification.
- Twisted thin wires for flexibility.

3 Daisy has two electric drills in her workshop. They have the following information stamped on them.

drill A

240V
a.c.
50Hz

drill B

12V
d.c.

a Which of these drill works directly from the 'mains'?

b What do the 3 terms mean on drill A?

c What might drill B run on?

d Which drill needs thicker insulation? Explain your answer.

e Which drill *might* need an earth wire in its cable? Explain your answer.

f Which drill would be safe to use in the rain? Explain your answer.

4 Copy this diagram of a correctly wired mains plug. Use the labels below in place of the letters A–E on your diagram.

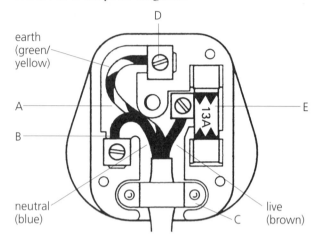

- Wires correctly positioned.
- Insulation cut back just enough – no bare wire showing.
- Cable clamp secure.
- Screws tightened.
- Correct fuse fitted.

5 This plug has been incorrectly (and dangerously) connected. List as many faults as you can; there are seven to find.

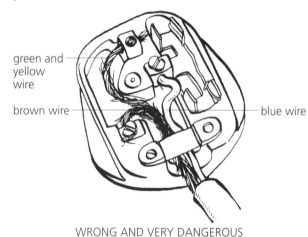

WRONG AND VERY DANGEROUS

130

1 Copy and complete the following sentences. Use the words below to fill the gaps.

wet   electricity   heart   contract

High voltage _____ can be very dangerous. If you get an electric shock, the electricity makes your muscles _____ . If this affects your _____ , it could kill you. If your hands or feet are _____ , more electricity flows through you so the danger is very much greater.

2 Copy and complete these sentences. Choose the correct word from each of the pairs given.

In mains electricity, the **live/neutral** wire provides the voltage that drives the current. If you touch a **live/neutral** wire you will get a shock. Because of this, switches should always be connected to the **live/neutral** wire. If the live and neutral wires are reversed in a plug, the equipment **will/will not work**, but it will not be safe.

3 Copy the diagrams. Use the labels below in place of the letters A–F on your diagram, to explain why the live and neutral wires must not be reversed.

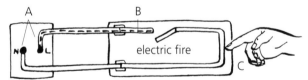

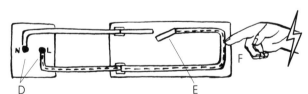

- The rest of the wire is live, even when the switch is open.
- Live current stops at the switch (when open).
- If you touch the wire, you will get a shock.
- Incorrectly wired.
- The rest of the wire is safe if touched.
- Correctly wired.

4 Fuses are connected in the live wire. If too great a current passes, they 'blow', switching off the circuit. Copy the diagrams. Use the labels below in place of the letters A–E on your diagram, to explain how fuses work.

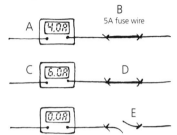

- Overload.
- Fuse wire breaks, breaking the circuit.
- Fuse wire cold.
- Working current.
- Fuse wire heats up.

5 Fuses come in set values: 13A, 5A and 2A. Copy and complete this table by adding the appropriate fuse to use in the plug.

Equipment	Working current	Fuse
a two-bar fire	8 A	a
radio	0.1 A	b
vacuum cleaner	3 A	c
freezer	2.5 A	d
small cooker	12 A	e
150 W bulb	0.6 A	f

6 Rearrange these sentences to explain how a residual current device (RCD) can protect you from a shock. Copy the sentences out in the correct order.

- The RCD detects that the current in the live wire is no longer the same as the current in the neutral wire.
- If a fault occurs, some current escapes through the earth wire – or through you.
- The RCD very quickly switches off the current.
- Normally the current in the live wire is the same as the current in the neutral wire.

1 Copy and complete the following sentences. Use the words below to fill the gaps.

repelled   magnet   pole   north   south

A .... will line up north–south if it is free to move. The end that points .... is called the north-seeking .... Magnets attract iron and steel. The north pole of one magnet will attract the .... pole of another, but if one magnet is turned round it will be ....

2 Copy and complete this sentence. Choose the correct word from each of the pairs given. You should be able to do this in two different ways, to make two correct sentences.

Like/Unlike poles **repel/attract**.

3 Copy the following diagram. Say whether there would be attraction or repulsion in each case.

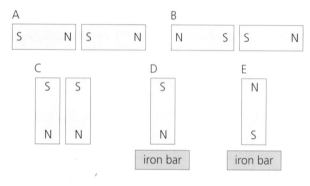

4 The magnet field around a magnet can be seen by sprinkling iron filings over it. A small compass needle will also follow these lines.

Copy the diagram. Show the direction in which a compass needle would point in the positions shown. (One has been done for you.)

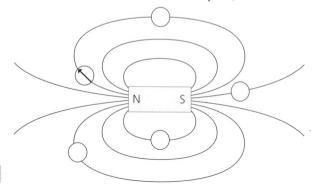

5 Hardeep made an electromagnet from a coil of wire, using 10 turns, and connected it up as shown.

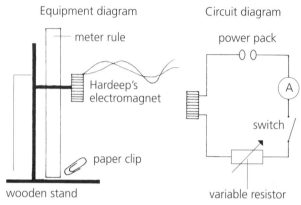

She used the electromagnet to investigate how high paper clips could be made to jump for different currents. The table below shows her results.

Current	Height (mm)
0.3	11
0.6	20
1.0	35
1.5	50
1.6	42
2.0	72

a Plot a scatter graph of her results, showing current against height jumped.

b Her friend Suzie changed the rheostat in the middle of one reading, so Hardeep wrote down the wrong current value. Draw a circle around this anomaly (the point that does not fit the pattern).

c Draw a best fit straight line through the rest of the points.

d Describe the relationship between the height jumped and the current.

e Sketch in a new line to suggest the results you might expect if she repeated the experiment using 20 turns instead of 10.

f Eric did a similar experiment, but wound his coils around an iron nail, which he left in place. Would his electromagnet have been stronger or weaker?

1 Copy and complete the following sentences. Use the words below to fill the gaps.

iron   permanent   electromagnets

Unlike .... magnets, ... can be switched off. This is very useful for buzzers and relays, as well as the giant magnets used to lift scrap ....

2 Look at the car starter motor circuit.

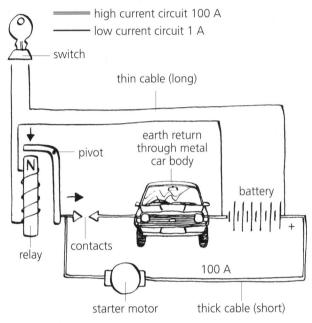

a What happens to the relay coil when the switch is turned on?

b What happens to the pivoted iron plate?

c What happens to the contacts after part **b**?

d What happens to the starter motor after part **c**?

e Why does the starter motor circuit need thicker cable than the switch circuit?

3 In a simple electric motor, a coil spins in a magnetic field. What would happen to the spinning motor if

a the current was increased

b the current was reversed?

4 Rearrange the following sentences to explain how a loudspeaker works. Copy the sentences out in the correct order.

- The coil becomes an electromagnet, its strength varying with the current.
- The coil moves a paper cone in and out.
- This makes the coil move backwards and forwards, to the same pattern as the electrical signal.
- The moving paper cone makes the air vibrate, creating sound waves.
- A varying force occurs between the electromagnet and the permanent magnet.
- A variable electrical signal is passed through a coil that is held loosely in a magnetic field from a permanent magnet.

5 **a** Rearrange the sentences to describe how the buzzer works. Copy the sentences out in the correct order.

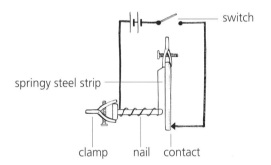

- This breaks the circuit at the contact.
- The springy steel vibrates backwards and forwards as the current is switched on and off at the contact.
- When the switch is closed, current flows in the circuit.
- The steel springs back, making the circuit again.
- The springy steel is attracted to the electromagnet.
- The coil becomes an electromagnet.
- The coil loses its magnetism.

b Why is the coil of the electromagnet wound round an iron nail?

1 Copy and complete this sentence. Choose the correct word from each of the pairs given. You should be able to do this in two different ways, to make *two* correct sentences.

A **generator / motor** turns **kinetic / electrical** energy into **kinetic / electrical** energy.

2 Look at the diagram of a magnet being pushed into a coil of wire. Answer the following questions, thinking about the size *and* direction of any current produced.

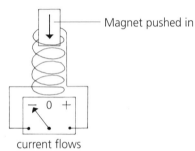

Magnet pushed in

current flows

What would happen if the magnet was.....
a left in the coil (not moving)
b pulled out
c pushed in faster
d pulled out of a coil with twice as many turns?

3 Look at the diagram, which shows a cross section of a coil turning between two magnets. The magnets are standing vertically, and the coil rotates about a horizontal axis. The current produced in one part of
the coil is shown, as the coil turns through 360°.

Copy the diagram. Use the labels (at the top of the next column) in place of the letters A–D on your diagram.

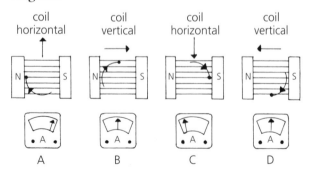

coil horizontal	coil vertical	coil horizontal	coil vertical
A	B	C	D

- When the wire runs parallel to the field there is no current.
- When the wire cuts down through the field a reverse current is induced.
- When the wire cuts up through the field a current is induced.
- When the wire runs parallel to the field there is no current.

4 Copy and complete the following sentences. Choose the correct word from each of the pairs given.

Electrical generators work by having a coil of wire spinning in a magnetic field. The size of the voltage induced can be increased by spinning **slower / faster**, having **more / fewer** turns in the coil and using a **stronger / weaker** magnetic field.

5 Melissa measured the voltage induced as a coil was spinning between two magnets. Here are her results for one complete turn.

Degrees rotation	Voltage (V)
0	0
45	7
90	10
135	7
180	0
225	-7
270	-10

a Plot a graph of her results, drawing a smooth curve through the points.
b What type of electricity does this show?
c Annotate the graph to show a point where the coil was cutting across the magnetic field at right angles.
d Annotate the graph to show a point where the coil was running parallel to the magnetic field.
e Rotating coils like this are used to generate electricity, but if fixed wire connections were used they would twist up and break. Explain how slip-rings and brushes are used to take the current away from the coil.

1 Copy and complete this sentence. Choose the correct word from each of the pairs given. You should be able to do this in two different ways, to make *two* correct sentences.

Like/Unlike charges **repel/attract**.

2 A freshly rubbed comb will pick up small pieces of paper. Copy the diagram. Use the labels below in place of the letters A–D on your diagram.

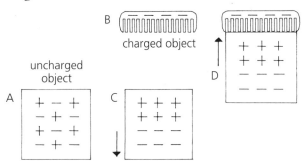

- The remaining positive charges are attracted to the comb.
- A charged comb has an excess of negative charges.
- The comb charge repels the negative charges on the paper.
- An uncharged object has positive and negative charges.

3 Copy and complete the following sentences. Choose the correct word (or words) from each of the pairs given.

If you touch a charged van der Graaff generator, your hair **stands on end/lies flat.** This is because all the hairs become charged with **the same/different** charges, and these **unlike/like** charges repel each other.

4 Use the idea of static electricity to explain the following situations.

a Electrostatics are used to ensure that spray paint spreads out evenly. (Clue: the paint droplets all pick up the same charge.)
b Your hair can sometimes stand up in a thunderstorm or when you take off a nylon jumper.

5 Rearrange these sentences to explain what electrolysis is and how it works. Copy the sentences out in the correct order.

- Simpler substances are then released at the electrodes.
- If electrodes are put into this ionic liquid, a current flows.
- Some compounds are made of electrically charged particles called ions.
- The positive ions move to the negative electrode, while the negative ions move to the positive electrode.
- If the compound dissolves in water or melts, these ions become free.

6 If copper sulphate solution is electrolysed copper is deposited at the negative electrode. In an experiment, 2 g of copper were deposited after 5 minutes.

a How much copper would you expect to get in 10 minutes, for the same current?
b How much copper would you expect to get in 5 minutes if the current was halved.
c How much copper would you expect to get for double the current in 1 hour?

7 Copy the diagram of a van der Graaff generator. Use the labels below in place of the letters A–C on your diagram to explain what is happening.

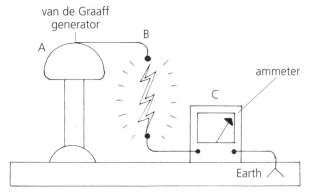

- Once the voltage is high enough, a spark will jump the air gap.
- As charge builds up on the dome, the voltage increases.
- Electric current is detected as electrons flow through the metal wire to earth.

1 Copy and complete the following sentences. Use the words below to fill the gaps.

charge   amps   energy

The current in a circuit is measured in
.... This is the rate of flow of electrical
.... The voltage measures the ....
carried by the charge.

2 Copy and complete the following sentences. Choose the correct word from each of the pairs given.

The size of the **current/voltage** flowing in a simple circuit depends on the resistance. A low resistance lets a **low/high** current flow. But the size of the current also depends on the voltage. The higher the voltage the **higher/lower** the current.

3 In a circuit, what would happen to the size of the current if you

a doubled the voltage
b doubled the resistance
c multiplied the resistance by 10?

4 Look at this graph showing how the current in a circuit varies with voltage.

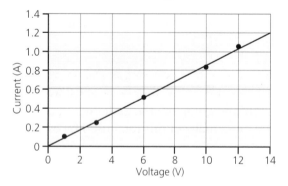

a Describe in words how the current varies with the voltage.
b What is the current at 6 V?
c What would the current be at 8 V?
d What current would you expect at 14 V?
e What voltage gives a current of 1 A?
f What is the resistance of this circuit? (Use your answer to part **d**, and the formula resistance = voltage/current. You will need to use a calculator.

5 Look at this circuit diagram.

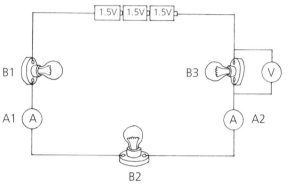

a What is the total voltage from the three cells?
b If ammeter A1 reads 0.5 A, what is the current at A2?
c The three bulbs are identical and B1 has a resistance of 3 ohms. What is the total resistance of the three bulbs in this circuit?
d If voltmeter V reads 1.5 V, what would the reading be across bulb B1?
e A current of 0.5 A flows through B3. Calculate its resistance. (Resistance = voltage/current.) Does this agree with part **c**?

6 Look at this circuit diagram. B1, B2 and B3 are identical, 4 ohm bulbs.

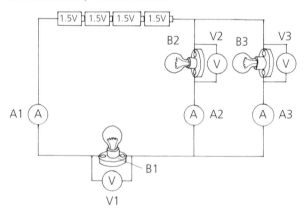

a Is this a series or parallel circuit?
b If ammeter A1 reads 1 A, what is the current through A2?
c What is the current through A3?
d What is the total voltage provided by the four cells?
e Voltmeter V2 reads 2 V. What does V3 read?
f What must V1 read?
g Is the *combined* resistance of bulbs B2 and B3 larger, smaller or equal to that of bulb B1?

1 Copy and complete the following sentences. Use the words below to fill the gaps.

transformer   down   alternating   up

The generators in a power station produce .... current. This is stepped .... to a very high voltage by a .... before it is sent through the National Grid. Other transformers then step .... the voltage to safer levels before the electricity is sent to your home.

2 Copy the diagram of the energy transfers in a power station. Use the labels below in place of the letters A–D on your diagram.

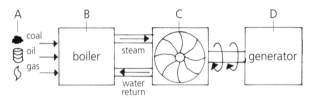

- Water is boiled by this energy.
- The turbine spins a generator which generates electricity.
- The expanding steam turns a turbine.
- Fuels are burnt to release their stored energy.

3 The National Grid carries electricity at a very high voltage – up to 132 000 V or more. This must be changed back to a lower voltage by a step-down transformer.

a Why do the National Grid cables have to be so high up in the air?

b Why are the cables held away from the metal pylon by very thick insulating plates?

c Why does the voltage have to be reduced before it goes to your home?

d Transformers are not 100% efficient – they lose some of the useful energy. How could you tell this if you stood near a transformer?

4 Look at the pie chart showing the way useful energy is lost in a power station.

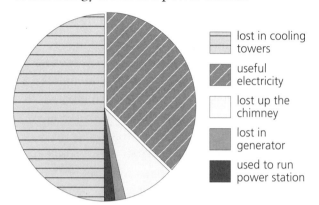

- lost in cooling towers
- useful electricity
- lost up the chimney
- lost in generator
- used to run power station

a What fraction of the total energy is lost from the cooling towers?

b Which is the next highest energy loss?

c The 'used' steam is sometimes pumped to greenhouses as hot water instead of being sent up the cooling towers. What is it used for?

d Why is this a good idea – apart from its use in the greenhouse?

5 Look at the table, showing how electrical energy is used in Britain.

Sector	Amount used (10^{15} J)	%
industry	331	
homes	380	
other	289	
total		

a Which sector uses the most electricity?

b What is the total amount of electricity used?

c Copy and complete the table by calculating the percentage of this total used by each sector.

$$\% = \frac{\text{amount used}}{\text{total amount}} \times 100\%$$

d Draw a pie chart from these figures.

e Some people do not bother about saving electricity at home. They say that the amount they could save is so small that it wouldn't make a difference. Use your answer to part **a** to help explain why this view is wrong.

1 Copy and complete the following sentences. Use the words below to fill the gaps.

transformer   power   low   high

You can get the same .... from an electrical circuit by having a low current at a .... voltage or a high current at a .... voltage. With a.c. you can change between these different situations by using a ....

2 Copy the diagram of a transformer. Use the labels below in place of the letters A–C on your diagram.

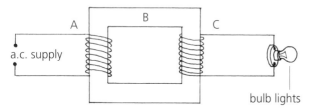

bulb lights

• The iron core links the field to the two coils.
• The primary coil produces a changing magnetic field.
• The secondary coil has an alternating current induced in it.

3 Look at the diagram of a 1:4 step-up transformer.

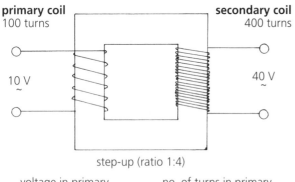

primary coil
100 turns

secondary coil
400 turns

10 V

40 V

step-up (ratio 1:4)

$$\frac{\text{voltage in primary}}{\text{voltage in secondary}} = \frac{\text{no. of turns in primary}}{\text{no. of turns in secondary}}$$

What would the output (secondary) voltage be if the input voltage was changed to:
a 50 V?
b 25 V?
c 1 V?
d If the output (secondary) voltage was 160 V, what must the input (primary) voltage have been?
e Draw a scatter graph of secondary voltage plotted against primary voltage for this transformer. Draw a line through your points.
f Sketch in a second line that would show the output voltage if the secondary coil only had 200 turns instead of 400.

4 Copy and complete this table showing information about different transformers.

Primary voltage	Primary turns	Secondary turns	Secondary voltage
10	100	600	**a**
12	600	100	**b**
c	200	800	200
d	800	200	100
15	600	**e**	5
15	600	**f**	30
2	100	**g**	20
25	500	**h**	5

5 Rearrange these sentences to explain how an electric welder works. Copy the sentences out in the correct order.

• This induces a much lower voltage in the thick-wired secondary coil.
• But current goes up as voltage goes down.
• The transformer has many times fewer turns in the secondary coil.
• This heating effect is great enough to melt and weld metal.
• Mains electricity passes into a transformer.
• The very high secondary current has a very high heating effect.

1 Copy this formula that shows how to calculate the power in an electrical circuit:

power (W) = voltage (V) x current (A)
(watts)   (volts)   (amps)

What is the power of a motor that runs on 10 V and takes a 2 A current?

2 Copy and complete the following sentences. Choose the correct word from each of the pairs given.

A **resistor/diode** allows current to flow in either direction. A **resistor/diode** allows current to flow in one direction only.

3 **a** Copy and complete this table showing current, voltage and power data from various electrical circuits. Use the formula from **Q1** to calculate the missing values.

Voltage (V)	Current (A)	Power (W)
240	10	i
240	0.25	ii
12	5	iii
110	iv	1100
24	v	12
1.5	vi	6
vii	5	30
viii	3	72
ix	0.1	24

b Which *three* entries could refer to 'mains' circuits?

c Which fuse would you use in each circuit from part **b**? (Choose from 2A, 5A or 13A.)

d Which might be an electric kettle circuit?

e Which might be an electric light bulb circuit?

4 The circuit (at the top of the next column) was used to test both a lamp and a diode. Each component was placed in position X. Each component was connected one way and then the connections were reversed. The voltage was changed at the power supply. The current and voltage readings are shown in the table (in the next column).

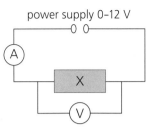
power supply 0–12 V

Voltage (V)	Current in component A (amps)		Current in component B (amps)	
	normal	reversed	normal	reversed
0	0	0	0	0
2	0.4	-0.4	0.2	0
4	0.7	-0.7	0.4	0
6	0.87	-0.87	0.6	0
8	0.95	-0.95	0.8	0
10	1.0	-1.0	1.0	0

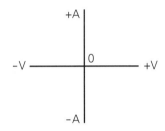

a Plot the results for component A on a graph with axes as shown.

b Plot the results for component B on a similar graph.

c Label your graphs 'lamp' or 'diode' as appropriate.

d For your 'lamp' graph describe the way the current varies as the voltage increases. Explain why this is happening.

e For your 'diode' graph, how do you know that this graph represents a diode?

f Describe how the current varies with voltage when the diode is connected the right way around.

g Resistance in ohms = voltage (V) / current (A).
What is the resistance of the lamp at 2 V?

h Calculate the resistance for the lamp at 4 V, 6 V, 8 V and 10 V.

i Plot a graph of resistance against voltage for the lamp.

j What is the resistance of the diode when it is connected the right way round?

1 Jamil measured the current through and the voltage across a resistor and recorded his results.

Voltage (V)	Current (A)
2.50	0.04
4.10	0.07
5.90	0.10
9.70	0.16
11.50	0.19

a Plot a graph of his results, with current as the x axis.
b Draw a 'best fit' straight line through his points.
c Comment on the accuracy of his readings.
d Use the graph to estimate the current at 8 V.
e Extrapolate the graph to estimate the likely current at 15 V.
f Do you think your answer to part **e** is a reliable as your answer to part **d**? Explain your view.
g Construct lines on your graph and use them to work out the gradient of the line.
h What is this gradient equal to?
i Sketch in and label the line you would expect for a resistor of double the resistance.
j Sketch in and label the line you would expect for a resistor of half the resistance.

2 Look at this graph, which shows how the resistance of a certain thermistor drops with temperature.

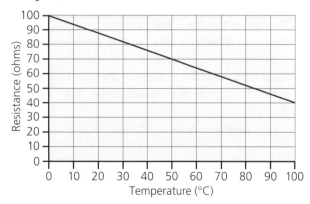

a What is the resistance at 75 °C?
b At what temperature is the resistance 85 ohms?
c What current would flow though the thermistor circuit at 0 °C if it were connected to a 12 V battery?

The thermistor could be set up as part of a frost prevention circuit for a greenhouse, as shown below. The computer would sense the current flowing in the circuit.

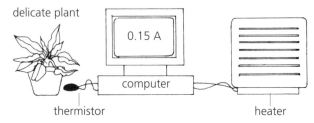

delicate plant   heater
          thermistor   computer

d How would the computer know when to switch the heater on?
e If the temperature must not rise above 25 °C, how would the computer know when to switch the heater off?
f Draw a conversion graph for current against temperature for this circuit.

3 A heating coil, used to heat up a beaker of water, runs at 0.2 A for 1 minute.

a How much charge passes through the circuit in this time?
charge in coulombs (C) = current (A)
x time (s)
b If the coil is running at 12 V, how much energy has been transferred to the water in this time?
energy (J) = voltage (V) x coulombs (C)
c Calculate the power generated by this circuit.
power (W) = voltage (V) x current (A)

The energy transferred is given by the formula
energy (J) = power (W) x time (s)

d Use this formula to work out the energy transferred to the water in 1 minute. Does it agree with your answer to part **b**?
e Find the charge, power and energy transferred in a circuit where a 9 V battery drives a current of 0.5 A through a bulb for 5 minutes.
f Perform a *similar* set of calculations to find the current, charge and energy transferred in a 3 kW mains electric heater (240 V) running for 1 hour.

1 The letters in the following words have been scrambled up. Unscramble them to find words that can be used when we want to describe the way things are moving.

**aeltarecec epdse toircedin adncsite
meit   yevoiltc**

2 The table below (at the bottom of the page) contains data about some cars.

Use the data in the table to answer the following questions:
a Which car
  i is the heaviest
  ii has the greatest fuel consumption
  iii has the highest top speed
  iv accelerates most slowly from 0 to 60mph
  v is the most powerful?

b Gemma says 'The bigger the engine, the faster the car'.
Draw up a table with three columns, headed model, engine size (cc) and 0–60 mph (seconds). Fill in your table using data about the cars, putting them in order of engine size. Is Gemma right?
c Each car is driven on a journey of 200 miles.
  i Calculate how much fuel each car would use on this journey.
  ii If a gallon of fuel costs £3.50, calculate the cost of the fuel for the journey for each car.
d Plot bar charts for the
  i power output
  ii 0–60 mph
  iii maximum speed
  data for each car. Put the names of the cars on the x-axis for each chart.
e Compare the shape of the three charts from part **d**. Is there any link between these three ways of measuring the performance of a car? What advice would you give someone buying a car?

Manufacturer	Model	Weight (kg)	Maximum speed (mph)	0–60 mph (seconds)	Fuel consumption (mpg)	Engine size (cc)	Power output (bhp)
Audi	2.8SE	1450	143	8.1	30.0	2771	193
BMW	318tds	1340	113	13.0	46.8	1665	90
Citroen	Xantia 2.0iSX	1238	122	9.6	33.2	1998	135
Ford	Mondeo 24V Ghia X	1377	131	8.4	30.0	2544	167
Isuzu	Trooper 3.2 V6 LWB	1880	106	11.4	19.3	3165	174
Lada	Samara 1.1 3dr	900	85	16.7	37.5	1099	53
Mazda	MX5 1.8i S	990	116	9.9	32.0	1839	130
Nissan	Micra 1.3 GX 3 dr	810	104	10.6	46.3	1275	75
Porsche	Targa	1370	168	5.2	25.2	3600	285
Rover	216 Sli 5dr	1040	113	8.9	40.8	1589	109

1 Copy and complete the following sentences. Use the words below to fill the gaps.

fast   constant   distance   stationary steeper

When an object is moving, its speed describes how .... it is travelling. Its movement can be plotted on a .... – time graph. Where the graph is straight, the object is moving at a .... speed. Where the graph is horizontal, the object is .... The .... the slope of the graph, the greater the speed.

2 Copy the four distance–time graphs and then answer the following questions. Explain each answer.

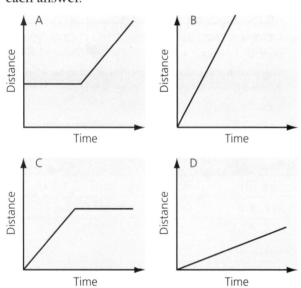

a Which graph shows an object which moves at a steady speed to start with and then stops?
b Which graph shows an object which is moving at a steady speed faster than all the others?
c Which graph shows an object which is moving at a steady speed slower than all the others?
d Which graph shows an object which is stationary to begin with and then moves away at a steady speed?

3 Calculate the speed of the following

a a sprinter who runs 100 m in 10 s
b a ball which moves 18 m in 6 s
c an aeroplane which flies 10 000 m in 50 s
d a snail which travels 1 m in 500 s
e a car which travels 5.4 km in 30 minutes.

4 The graph shows the movement of a mouse travelling in a straight line away from its nest.

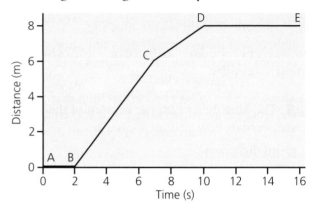

a Describe the movement of the mouse in words.
b Calculate the speed of the mouse between points B and C.
c Calculate the speed of the mouse between C and D.

5 Malik and Susan investigated how fast they could roller skate. Their results are shown in the table. Plot a graph of these results using suitable axes. Show clearly which line is Malik's and which is Susan's.

| Time (s) | Distance from start (m)... | |
	Malik	**Susan**
0	0	0
2	4	5
4	8	10
6	12	15
8	16	20
10	20	25
12	24	29
14	24	33
16	24	37
18	26	41
20	28	44
22	30	47
24	34	50
26	38	50
28	42	50
30	46	50
32	50	50

1 Copy and complete the following definitions. Use the words below to fill the gaps.

distance   acceleration   velocity   speed

- If an object moves in a straight line, how far it is from a certain point is described as the .... it has travelled.
- The .... of an object travelling in a straight line measures how fast it is travelling.
- The .... of an object is its speed in a given direction.
- The .... of an object is the rate at which its velocity changes.

2 Copy the four velocity–time graphs and then answer the following questions. Explain your answer in each case.

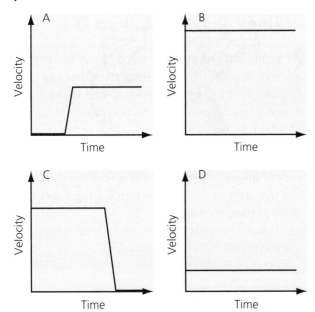

a Which graph shows an object which moves at a steady speed to start with and then slows to a stop?
b Which graph shows an object which is moving at a steady speed faster than all the others?
c Which graph shows an object which is moving at a steady speed slower than all the others?
d Which graph shows an object which is stationary to begin with and then moves away at a steady speed?

3 The graph shows Hamish's journey to the local shop on foot. Copy the graph. Then copy and complete the table, describing Hamish's motion in words as clearly as you can.

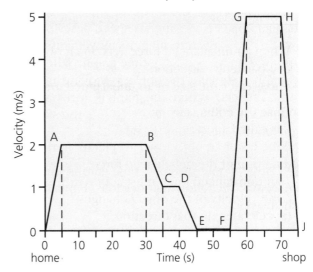

Part of graph	Hamish's motion
0 to A	
A to B	
B to C	
C to D	
D to E	
E to F	
F to G	
G to H	
H to J	

4 Calculate the following accelerations

a a cat which increases its speed from 0 to 2 m/s in 1 s
b a gymnast who increases her speed from 1 m/s to 4 m/s in 0.5 s
c a car slowing down from 15 m/s to rest in 5 s
d a cyclist slowing down from 4 m/s to 2.5 m/s in 3 s
e a bird of prey, hovering and then reaching a diving speed of 12 m/s in 1.5 s.

5 From the graph in **Q3** calculate Hamish's acceleration between each pair of points on the graph (0 and A, A and B, and so on).

4 Changing motion

1 Copy and complete the following sentences, choosing the correct ending in each case.

a To change an object's speed.....
b A push or a pull.....
c When the forces acting on a body cancel out they.....
d When an unbalanced force acts on an object in a particular direction.....
e The greater the size of an unbalanced force......

Choose the endings from:
- .....is called a force.
- .....the faster an object will accelerate in the direction of the unbalanced force.
- .....an unbalanced force must act on it.
- .....the velocity of the object changes (accelerates) in that direction.
- .....are said to be balanced.

2 'When an object rests on a surface, it pushes downwards on the surface. The surface pushes upwards on the object. The sizes of the two pushes are the same.'

Copy out these sentences and draw a diagram to show the forces acting on a book as it rests on the surface of a table. Use arrows like this: ↓

Use the length of each arrow to represent the size of the force.

3 Copy the diagrams. On each diagram, show the horizontal forces acting on the bicycle, using arrows like this: ➡

Use the length of each arrow to represent the size of the force.

A

steady speed

B

steady speed, but into a headwind

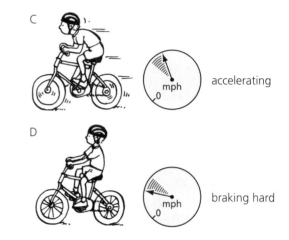

C

accelerating

D

braking hard

4 The picture shows a race with two go-carts.

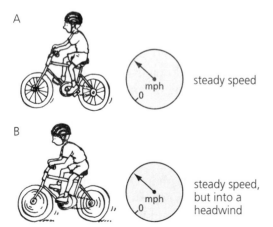

Draw diagrams to show the horizontal and vertical forces acting on each go-cart
a at the start of the race (when each go-cart has just started to move)
b half-way through the race (when each go-cart is travelling at a steady speed).
c Who do you think will win the race, and why?

5 Answer the following questions, using the relationship

force (N) = mass (kg) × acceleration (m/s²)

a A car has a mass of 750 kg and accelerates at a rate of 3 m/s². What is the size of the unbalanced force acting on it?
b A person pushes a supermarket trolley full of shopping. The mass of the trolley and shopping is 50 kg, and the unbalanced force acting on it is 200 N. What is its acceleration?

1 Copy and complete the following sentences. Choose the correct phrase in **bold** in each case.

Frictional forces always act when **an object is moving / an object is not moving**. These frictional forces are caused by **solid surfaces getting hot / solid surfaces in contact with one another** and by the resistance of air or water pushing backwards on the object. The direction of the frictional force **is opposite to the direction in which the object is moving / does not depend on the direction in which the object is moving**. The friction between solid surfaces is used **in car engines to produce heat / in car brakes to slow down and stop moving cars**. Friction causes objects to **heat up and wear away / stop working properly**.

2 Copy and complete the table to show how friction is made as large as possible in some places, and as small as possible in others.

Place	Size of frictional force	How is the frictional force controlled?
car engine		
road surface		
sole of shoe		

3 **a** Copy and complete these sentences (you will need to add more than one word in each case).
i Thinking distance is the distance travelled....
ii Braking distance is the distance travelled....
iii If you add together the thinking distance and the braking distance, you get the....
b List two factors that can increase
i thinking distance
ii braking distance.

4 'Only a fool breaks the two second rule' is a saying designed to help car drivers leave a large enough gap between their car and the car in front. A 'two second gap' is the distance travelled by a car in two seconds. The table shows some stopping distances for cars travelling at different speeds.

Speed (m/s)	Total stopping distance (m)	'Two second gap' (m)
11	12	
27	53	
37	96	

a Copy and complete the table to show how long a 'two second gap' is for each speed.
b Does a 'two second gap' provide a safe stopping distance for each speed in the table? Explain your answer.
c When might you have to leave a larger gap, even at slower speeds?

1 Rearrange the sentences below to explain how the braking system of a car works. Copy the sentences out in the correct order. Use the diagram of the braking system to help you.

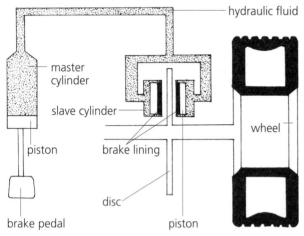

- The hydraulic fluid exerts a force on the piston in the slave cylinder.
- The force on the piston in the master cylinder increases the pressure in the hydraulic fluid.
- Driver pushes on brake pedal – this pushes on the piston in the master cylinder.
- The force on the piston in the slave cylinder pushes the brake pads against the disc.
- The hydraulic fluid transmits pressure equally in all directions.

2 **a** Why do vehicles that are designed to travel over soft ground have wide tyres?
b Why can wide planks of wood be used to rescue a person who has fallen through thin ice?
c Why does a drawing pin have a small point at one end and a broad top at the other end?

3 A person leans against a wall, pressing on it with the palm of one hand, which has an area of 50 cm².

a If they exert a force of 200 N on the wall, calculate the pressure they exert on the wall, using the formula: pressure = force / area

Write your answer using the correct units.

b The person now reduces the force they exert on the wall to 50 N. However, they now press with one fingertip, with an area of 1 cm². Calculate the new pressure exerted on the wall.

4 The deepest part of any ocean is thought to be the Marianas Trench in the Pacific Ocean, which is 11 000 m deep. At the bottom of the trench, the water pressure is 110 000 000 Pa! What force would this pressure exert on each 1 cm² area of a fish living at this depth?

5 Here are two possible designs for a hydraulic system designed to lift a weight of 720 N.

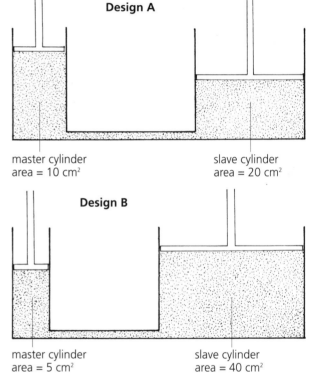

a Design A has one advantage over design B. What is it?
b Design B has one advantage over design A. What is it?

6 Airliners have pressurised cabins to enable passengers to be comfortable at altitudes of 10 000 m or more, where the air pressure outside the aircraft is 28 kPa. If the pressure in the cabin is 100 kPa, what is the resultant force on the cabin door in the side of an airliner? The door has an area of 2 m².

1 Copy and complete the following sentences. Use the words below to fill the gaps.

frictional mass accelerates terminal newtons gravitational

Wherever it is, an object always has the same .... , which is measured in kilograms. In a .... field an object will also have weight, which is measured in ....

There is a gravitational field around the Earth, which .... falling objects. As the speed of a falling object increases, ... forces increase until they balance the gravitational force.

When this happens, the balanced forces acting on the object mean that its speed does not increase any more – it has reached .... velocity.

2 Copy the pictures of the skydiver and the force arrows, putting them in the correct order to describe what happens during a parachute jump.

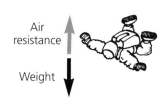

3 Describe how a parachute makes it possible to jump out of an aeroplane safely. Use the following words:

terminal velocity air resistance frictional forces weight

4 Calculate the weight of the following at the surface of the Earth, using the relationship

weight (N) = mass (kg) x gravitational field strength (N/kg).

a a 2 kg Christmas pudding
b a 750 kg car
c a 45 kg person.

Take the gravitational field strength at the surface of the Earth as 10 N/kg.

5 Weather balloons, filled with hydrogen, carry instruments high into the Earth's atmosphere to make measurements. Diagram A shows a weather balloon just about to be released at the Earth's surface, while diagram B shows the same balloon high above the Earth's surface. Using ideas about air pressure and the Earth's atmosphere, explain why the balloon looks different in the two diagrams.

6 A balloon is filled with air to a pressure of 1 atm. It has a volume of 1200 cm³. The balloon is taken up a mountain to a height where the atmospheric pressure is 0.6 atm. What is the volume of the balloon here?

7 The pressure of the gas in an oxygen cylinder is 300 atm. The cylinder has a volume of 0.4 m³. What volume would the oxygen occupy if it was let out of the cylinder into the atmosphere?

8 *Movement and energy*

1 Copy and complete the following sentences. Use the words below to fill the gaps.

fuel energy hot joules work force

When an object is moved by a force, the force does ...., and energy is transferred. The engine in a car provides the .... to make the car move. The moving car has kinetic energy. This energy comes from the mixture of .... and air which is burnt in the engine. When the driver brakes, the car slows down and the brakes get .... as .... is transferred from the car to the brakes. Both energy and work are measured in ....

2 Copy and complete the following sentences. Choose the correct phrase in **bold** in each case.

a As an object travels faster, its kinetic energy **stays the same / gets smaller / gets larger**.

b Two objects with different masses are travelling at the same speed. The kinetic energy of the larger mass is **the same as / greater than / less than** the kinetic energy of the smaller mass.

c A clockwork mouse is wound up and released. As it speeds up, the energy stored in the spring inside the mouse **decreases / does not change / increases**.

3 Use the relationship

work done (J) = force (N) × distance moved in direction of force (m)

to calculate the following

a the work done when a person lifts a 1 kg bag of sugar a distance of 2 m

b the work done when a 50 kg person climbs a flight of stairs 5 m high.

c Where does the energy to do this work come from in each case?

4 A car accelerates from rest up to a steady speed. A short time later, the brakes are applied, the car slows down, and then travels at a steady speed again.

a Draw an 'energy arrow' diagram to show what happens to the energy from the mixture of fuel and air burnt in the engine
  i as the car accelerates
  ii as the brakes are applied.

b When the car eventually stops, what will have happened to the energy from the mixture of fuel and air burnt in the engine?

5 Kinetic energy is calculated using the formula

kinetic energy (J) = ½ × mass (kg) × (velocity (m/s))²

A bullet has a mass of 0.025 kg and leaves the barrel of a gun at 300 m/s. A jet airliner has a mass of 150 000 kg and also travels at 300 m/s.

a Calculate the kinetic energy of the bullet and of the airliner.

b Why are their kinetic energies different, even though they are travelling at the same speed?

6 A 'superball' with a mass of 0.1 kg is lifted from the ground to a height of 2 m.

a Calculate the energy transferred to the ball in lifting it to this height.

The ball is now released.

b What will be its kinetic energy just before it hits the ground?

The ball hits the ground and rebounds to a height of 1.8 m.

c Calculate the energy stored in the ball at this height.

d What was the kinetic energy of the ball just after it rebounded?

e Explain the difference between your answers to parts **b** and **d**.

9 Forces and changing shape

1 Copy and complete the following sentences, choosing the correct ending in each case.

a A force.....

b An object will return to its original shape and size when the force is removed if it.....

c Extension.....

d When an object is stretched beyond its elastic limit it.....

e Energy transferred to an object beyond the elastic limit.....

Choose the endings from:

- .....is not deformed past its elastic limit.
- .....is the amount something has stretched.
- .....cannot be got back as useful work.
- .....can change the shape of an object.
- .....is permanently deformed.

2 Justin carried out an investigation to see how a spring could be stretched using a force. He used his results to plot the graph shown below.

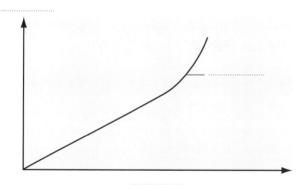

a Copy the graph and fill in the missing labels.

b Use the graph to help you to explain why a spring cannot be used any more if you stretch it too far.

c Using words and diagrams, describe the investigation you think Justin did.

3 Using words and diagrams, explain why crash barriers and cycle helmets are designed so that they are permanently deformed when they are damaged in an accident.

4 Sangeeta investigated what happened to a piece of elastic when it was stretched. She got the following results.

Force (N)	Extension (cm)
0	0
1	1.5
2	3.0
3	4.5
4	6.5
5	9.0

a Plot a graph of these results.

b Use your graph to estimate the extension of the elastic for a load of
i 0.5 N   **ii** 4.5 N.

5 Samantha and Panjid carried out an investigation to find out how two different springs stretched. Here are their results.

Force (N)	Length (cm)... Spring 1	Length (cm)... Spring 2
0	5.0	7.2
2	7.6	10.4
4	10.2	13.6
6	12.8	16.8
8	15.4	20.3
10	18.5	24.2

a Use these results to produce a graph to show the behaviour of the springs.

b Barry hung a weight on one of the springs. If the length of the spring was 13.2 cm, what possible values could the weight have had?

c Barry took the weights off both springs and then connected them together one underneath the other. He then hung a 5 N weight on them. How much did they stretch altogether?

10 Bringing it all together

1 Copy and complete the following sentences. Use the words below to fill the gaps.

**area   elastic   stretch   increases   limit
pressure   kinetic**

Modern cars have many safety features. Crumple zones are designed to 'fold up' if a car collides with something, transferring the car's .... energy to the car body. This deforms the car body beyond its .... limit. Padding inside the car helps to reduce the .... exerted by these parts of the car on the driver's body in an accident, by spreading the force over a bigger .... An airbag may help to protect the driver even more. As the driver's body compresses the gas in the bag, its pressure .... The bag pushes back on the driver's body, helping to slow it down. Seatbelts also help to slow the driver down. They .... as they stop the driver moving. This takes them beyond their elastic .... , so they must be replaced when the car is repaired after a serious accident.

2 The diagram shows a lap belt and a lap and diagonal belt. Which of these is do you think is safer? Explain your answer.

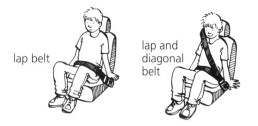

lap belt

lap and diagonal belt

3

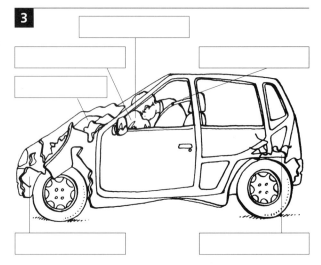

a Copy the diagram and fill in the missing labels to show the safety features fitted to this car.
b What other safety features do you think could be added? Explain these clearly, using diagrams and words.

4 Use the graph below to explain why wearing a seatbelt protects a passenger in a car when they are involved in a collision. Be as precise as you can, and use the data from the graph to make your points clearly.

Graph for **Q4**

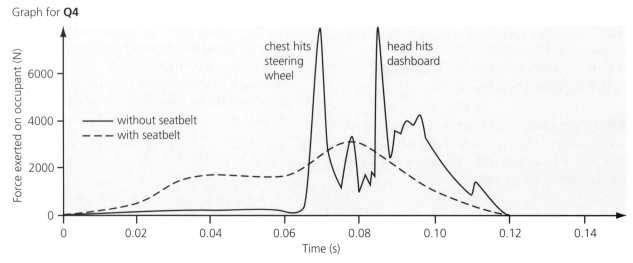

1 Copy and complete the following sentences. Use the words below to fill the gaps.

reflect 365 night constellations solar 24 daylight

The Earth spins once on its own axis every .... hours. The side of the Earth facing the Sun is in .... , while it is .... time in the half facing away from the Sun. The Earth takes .... days (one year) to make one complete orbit round the Sun. Seen from the Earth, the stars in the night sky form fixed patterns called .... We see the stars because they are like our Sun, giving off large amounts of light. The planets look just like stars, but they are really part of our .... system. We see them because they .... light from the Sun.

2 Draw a diagram including a torch and a ball to explain how the Earth's rotation causes day and night.

3 **a** Ancient peoples had very different ideas of the heavens to our modern views. Describe their ideas about the positions of the Earth, Sun and stars.
b The ancient Greeks observed some stars which moved differently to the other stars in the sky.
  i What name did the give these 'wandering stars'?
  ii Explain why these 'wandering stars' do not move like the other stars in the sky.

4 Artificial satellites can be used for weather forecasting, communications and observing space. For each use explain the advantages given by using a satellite.

5 In 1619 the German astronomer Johannes Kepler suggested the relationship

$$X = \frac{(\text{average distance from Sun})^3}{(\text{time for one orbit around Sun})^2}$$

where X is the same for all planets. Using this relationship you can calculate the distance of a planet from the Sun if you know the time it takes to orbit the Sun, or vice versa. The table below gives you some information.

Planet	Average distance from Sun (million km)	Time for one orbit around Sun (days)
Mercury	58	88
Venus	?	225
Earth	150	365
Mars	228	?
Jupiter	?	4330

a Find the value of X using the information for Mercury and Earth.
b Copy and complete the table.

1 Copy and complete the following sentences, choosing the correct ending in each case.

a The orbits of the planets.....

b All masses.....

c Pluto's orbit is so elliptical.....

d The greater the distance between two masses.....

e A smaller object can be made to orbit a larger object if.....

Choose the endings from:

- .....attract other masses with a force called gravity.
- .....the smaller the force of gravity between them.
- .....are ellipses (squashed circles).
- .....it has the right speed so that gravity pulls it towards the larger object and makes it travel in a circle.
- .....it is sometimes nearer the Sun than the planet Neptune is.

2 Copy the diagram and fill in the missing labels.

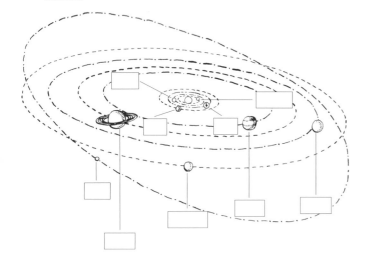

3 The diagram shows two satellites in orbit around the Earth. Satellite A orbits about 35 000 km above the Earth's equator, while satellite B orbits a few hundred km above the Earth, passing over the North and South poles.

a What is the likely use of satellite A?

b Explain how the orbit of satellite A makes it suitable for this use.

c What is the likely use of satellite B?

d Explain how the orbit of satellite B makes it suitable for this use

4 The diagram shows the part of a comet's orbit closest to the Sun.

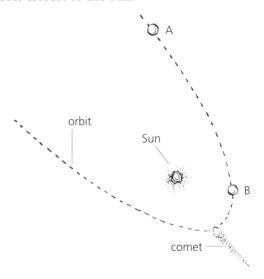

a Copy the diagram and show what the comet would look like at A and at B.

b Explain the comet's appearance at A and at B.

c Mark on your diagram with a letter X the point at which the comet is travelling fastest.

d Where in its orbit would the comet be travelling slowest?

1 Copy and complete the following sentences. Use the words below to fill the gaps.

ellipses galaxy Copernicus billions centre

In ancient times, people believed that the Earth was at the .... of the universe, with the Sun, Moon and stars rotating around it. In the sixteenth century, ... proposed that the Earth and other planets go round the Sun. We now know that the orbits of planets around the Sun are .... Our Sun is one star among .... , all held together by gravitational forces in a cluster known as a ....

2 According to the Big Bang model, the universe began in a huge explosion 15 000 million years ago. Use the information in the table to produce a time-line for the universe based on the Big Bang model.

Time after Big Bang	Event
1 000 million years	matter starts to clump together
5 000 million years	Milky Way forms
10 000 million years	Sun forms
10 400 million years	planets forms
12 000 million years	first life appears on Earth
14 800 million years	dinosaurs rule the Earth
14 998 million years	humans appear

3 The Milky Way contains between 100 and 200 billion stars. If 50% of these have planets of some sort, and the chance of finding life on one planet in a solar system is one in 10 billion, estimate how many other planets in the Milky Way might contain life.

4 The diagrams (at the top of the next column) show the spectra for three different stars seen from the Earth – the top spectrum is that of the Sun. The dark lines in the spectra are where light has been absorbed by helium atoms.

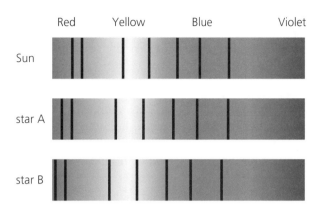

a Explain why the dark lines in the spectrum of a star may appear to be 'shifted'.
b Use the three spectra in the diagram to say as much as you can about star A and star B.

5 Astronomers can use parallax to measure how far an object is from the Earth. Hold up one finger in front of your nose. Now look at it, first with only your left eye and then with only your right eye. As you shut first one eye and then the other, your finger changes position against the background. The nearer your finger, the bigger the change in position. In just the same way, a nearby object appears to move against the background of very distant stars as the Earth goes round the Sun. If the distance from the Earth to the Sun is 150 million km, and the parallax angle of an object is 15°, how far away from the Earth is the object?
(Note: for even the nearest stars, the parallax angle is much smaller than this. The nearest star is Alpha Centauri, which is over 40 000 billion km away. The parallax angle for it is about 0.0002° !)

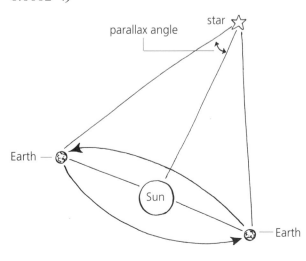

14 The secret life of stars

1 Rearrange these sentences to explain how stars form and then die. Copy the sentences out in the correct order.

- The star begins to use up its hydrogen, and the temperature at the core increases.
- The star fuses hydrogen to helium. The high temperatures which tend to make the star fly apart are balanced by enormous gravitational forces.
- The star swells up, its surface cools, and it becomes a red giant.
- A huge cloud of dust and hydrogen gas is pulled together by gravitational forces.
- The star cools and begins to collapse. What happens next depends on its mass – explosion as a supernova or forming a black hole are two possibilities.
- As the star forms, it heats up, until atoms of hydrogen can fuse together to form helium.

2 A science fiction story describes how a team of astronauts set out on a mission to explore a black hole. What do you think happens to them, and why?

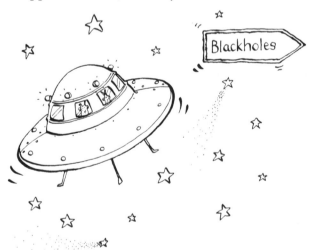

3 Explain, in terms of temperature and gravitational forces, why a star tends to expand and become a red giant when all its hydrogen is used up.

4 Design a poster to show how a star is formed from a cloud of dust and gas. Your poster should explain the following:

- where the matter that makes up the star comes from
- how the star begins to 'shine' (in other words, what makes it hot)
- how the star stays hot (in other words, what 'fuel' it uses)
- what stops the star flying apart or collapsing in on itself.

5 The Sun turns hydrogen into helium in a process called nuclear fusion, producing energy as it does so. About 600 billion kg of hydrogen is turned into helium by the Sun each second. How much hydrogen has the Sun converted into helium in your lifetime? Show your working clearly.

6 A star with a mass of 500 billion billion billion kg collapses, explodes as a supernova, and then forms a neutron star. If 25% of the original mass ends up in a neutron star 10 km in diameter

a calculate the density of the matter in the neutron star

b calculate the mass of 1 cm^3 of this matter.

1 Copy and complete the following sentences. Use the words below to fill the gaps.

straight electromagnetic waves speed energy

The Sun radiates energy, which is sometimes called _____ radiation. Different types of radiation are given different names, and they carry different amounts of _____ . All of them move as _____ , and travel in _____ lines at the same _____ .

2 Pair up the following statements about electromagnetic radiations so that the second statement follows from the first.

Statement 1

a The electromagnetic radiations all travel as waves.

b All electromagnetic radiations travel at the same speed.

c All electromagnetic radiations travel in straight lines.

d All electromagnetic radiations can travel through space.

Statement 2

• The electromagnetic radiations behave in similar ways.

• Infra-red radiation from the Sun can reach the Earth.

• Radio waves travel at the speed of light.

• It is impossible to see round corners.

3 The family of electromagnetic waves includes radio waves, microwaves, infra-red radiation, light and ultra-violet radiation. Copy the picture and fill in the labels to show where each type of radiation is being used.

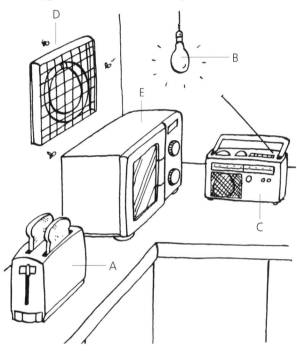

4 Electromagnetic waves travel through space at 300 000 km/s. Calculate how long it would take an electromagnetic wave to do the following journeys

a from a transmitter on the Earth to a satellite 30 000 km above the Earth's surface

b from the Moon to the Earth (about 390 000 km)

c from the Sun to the Earth (about 150 million km).

5 A light-year is a measure of distance. It is the distance travelled by light in 1 year. If light travels at 300 000 km/s, how far is a light-year? Give your answer in km.

2 Waves – what are they?

1 Copy and complete the following sentences. Use the words below to fill the gaps.

amplitude   frequency   wavelength energy

a A wave transfers .... from one place to another.
b The .... of a wave describes its maximum height.
c The .... of a wave describes the distance between a particular point on one disturbance and the same point on the next.
d The number of waves passing a particular point in one second is called the ....

2 Look at the diagram of a water wave shown in the diagram.

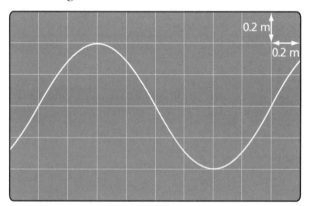

a What is the wave's amplitude?
b What is the wave's wavelength?

3 **a** Draw a water wave with an amplitude of 2 cm and a wavelength of 5 cm.
b Draw a water wave with both amplitude and frequency double the values of the wave in part **a**.

4 A boy pushes a ball up and down on the surface of a swimming pool to produce a wave, as shown in the picture.

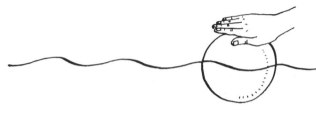

a The boy moves the ball further up and down, at the same rate as before. What happens to
 i the amplitude of the waves produced
 ii the wavelength of the waves produced
 iii the frequency of the waves produced?
b The boy moves the ball up and down the same distance as at first, but faster. What happens to
 i the amplitude of the waves produced
 ii the wavelength of the waves produced
 iii the frequency of the waves produced?

5 'The wave which travels along a rope is a transverse wave.'

a What is a transverse wave?
b How must you move the end of a long piece of rope to in order to produce a transverse wave?
c Which way do the particles in the rope move?

6 Explain why ripples on a pond make a leaf bob up and down, but the leaf hardly moves from side to side.

1 Copy and complete the following sentences. Use the words below to fill the gaps.

darker absorbed Sun light reflected

Waves can be _____ from hard surfaces. We see many objects because _____ is reflected from them and enters our eyes. We see other objects, like the _____ , because they give out their own light. When an object reflects light, some of the light may be _____ . The less light that is reflected, the _____ the object appears.

2 Copy and complete the diagram, showing the path of light waves A and B after reflection.

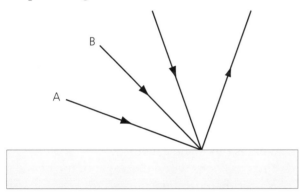

3 The diagram shows the Whispering Gallery in St Paul's Cathedral, London, which is circular.

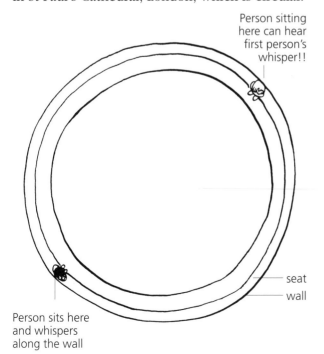

Person sitting here can hear first person's whisper!!

seat
wall

Person sits here and whispers along the wall

A person sitting on one side of the gallery can whisper a message along the wall of the gallery, and the message will be heard by another person sitting with their ear next to the wall on the opposite side of the gallery. Copy the diagram (at the bottom of the previous column) and use the idea of reflection to complete it.

4 A simple party trick involves sitting someone at a table, on which is a cup with a coin in it. The coin is just out of sight of the person, below the rim of the cup, as shown in the diagram. The person is asked to say what the coin is, without moving themselves or the cup. How can they do it? (Hint: a jug of water is placed on the table for them to use.) Draw a diagram to explain your suggestion. If in doubt, try the trick yourself!

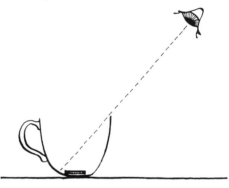

5 Copy and complete the table, suggesting what sort of wave might be involved in each case. Use the formula

velocity of wave (m/s) = frequency (Hz)
                          x wavelength (λ)

Velocity (m/s)	Frequency (Hz)	Wavelength (m)	Type of wave
3	a	10	b
c	200 000	1500	d
340	170	e	f

157

1 Copy and complete the following sentences and diagram. Use the words below to fill the gaps (one word is used more than once).

bent speed refracted ray normal incident ray

When light travels from one transparent material to another it may be .... This happens when the .... of light in one material is different to the .... of light in the other.

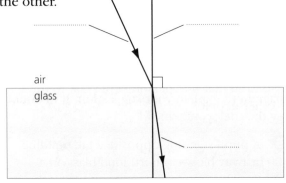

air
glass

2 Light bends towards the normal when it travels from air into glass, and away from the normal when it travels from glass into air. Copy and complete the diagram showing a ray of green light entering a triangular prism to show what happens when the light travels through the prism.

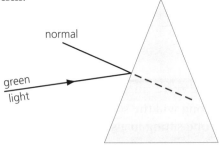

normal

green light

3 The diagram shows a ray of white light entering a prism.

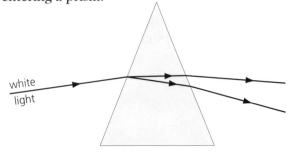

white light

a Light of seven different colours emerges from the prism. Why?
b Two rays are shown coming out of the prism. One is red, the other is violet – which is which?

4 A ray of light is shone through a semi-circular glass block, as shown in the diagram. Explain the following.

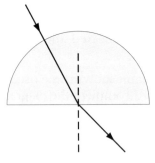

a The ray is not refracted as it enters the glass.
b The ray bends towards the glass as it leaves the block.

At a certain angle the refracted ray travels along the bottom of the glass.

c What is this angle called?
d What happens when the angle of incidence is greater than the angle in part **c**?

5 Draw diagrams to show how light travels along an optical fibre

a when the fibre is straight
b when it curves through an angle of 90°.

6 A periscope can be made from two prisms like the one shown below. Draw a diagram showing how the prisms must be arranged in order that someone can see over the heads of a crowd in front of them at a football match. Show the path of the light through the prisms, using rays with arrows on them.

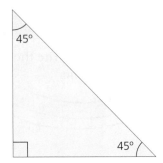

45°

45°

1 Copy and complete the following sentences. Use the words below to fill the gaps.

oscilloscope vibrating microphone energy

Like all waves, sound waves transfer _____ . This energy comes from objects which are _____ . Sound waves can be picked up by your ear and by a _____ . If this is connected to an _____ , a 'picture' of the sound wave can be obtained.

2 The diagram shows three oscilloscope traces produced by three different sound waves. The sounds are
- low pitch and loud
- low pitch and quiet
- high pitch and quiet.

A
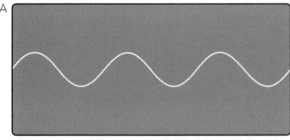

B
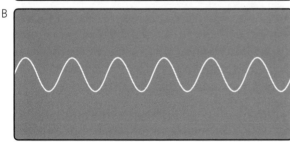

C
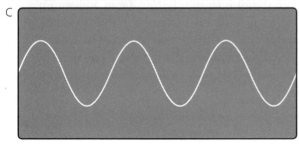

Copy the three traces and write the correct description under each one.

3 The 'string telephone' is a popular children's toy. It can be made from two plastic cups, joined together by a length of string, as shown in the diagram.

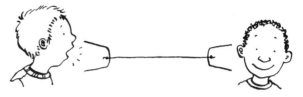

a Explain how the 'string telephone' works.
b Why must the string be tight?
c Why does the telephone stop working if someone holds the string?
d How could two of these string telephones be used so that one person could talk to three other people?

4 A pupil standing opposite a tall building 500 m away blows a short, loud blast on a whistle. The time from the blast to the echo is 3.0 s. What is the speed of sound?

5 A person sitting in a metal boat hits the hull of the boat, producing a sound wave that travels though the water and through the air.

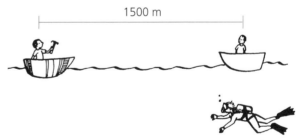

a How long will the sound take to reach someone sitting in a second boat 1500 m away?
b How much sooner will the sound be heard by a diver in the water underneath the second boat?

(Speed of sound in air = 340 m/s, speed of sound in water = 1500 m/s)

1 Copy and complete the following sentences. Use the words below to fill the gaps.

bats 20 000 Hz hear echo ultrasound echo location

When sound is reflected it is called an .... Some animals, like .... , make use of sound to 'see' – this is called .... They produce pulses of very high-pitched sound, called .... , which has a frequency of more than .... Humans cannot .... these pulses.

2 The diagram shows packets of cereal travelling along a conveyor belt. The ultrasound beam is used to count the numbers going past. How does this work?

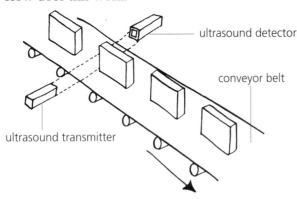

3 How is ultrasound used during a woman's pregnancy?

4 The diagram (at the top of the next column) shows a fishing trawler using pulses of sound to locate shoals of fish. Take the speed of sound in water as 1500 m/s.

a A pulse of sound is produced by the trawler. It travels down through the sea and bounces off the sea bed, returning to the trawler 0.2 s after it was produced. What is the depth of the sea? (Remember that the pulse goes down to the sea bed and back in 0.2 s.)

b How long after the pulse was produced would an echo be heard if it bounces off a shoal of fish 50 m below the surface?

c Another trawler produces a pulse of ultrasound, and two echoes are heard, one after 0.1 s and another after 0.4 s. Can you explain this?

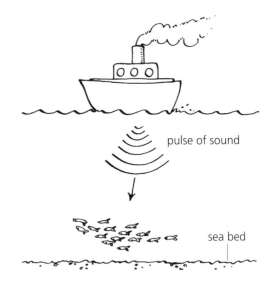

pulse of sound

sea bed

5 Ultrasound can be used to check that a metal casting (produced by pouring molten metal into a mould) contains no flaws, such as air bubbles.

a Why might these flaws be difficult to detect without using ultrasound?

b Explain very carefully how the ultrasound scan of a casting containing a flaw might differ from one which contains no flaw.

6 Some archaeologists know that a block of stone they have excavated from a tomb contains a rare jewel somewhere inside it. The block is a cube, exactly 1 m x 1 m x 1 m, and they decide to use ultrasound to locate the jewel.

Using a combined ultrasound transmitter and receiver, three separate ultrasound pulses are projected into the block, one at a time. This is done in such a way that each pulse is at right angles to the other two pulses. The table shows the time taken for each pulse to be detected.

Pulse 1	Pulse 2	Pulse 3
0.0004 s	0.000 08 s	0.000 72 s

The velocity of sound in the block is 2500 m/s.

Draw a diagram of the block, showing
a the direction of the three ultrasound pulses – label these 1, 2 and 3
b how far the jewel is from the places where the three pulses start.

1 Copy and complete the following sentences. Use the words below to fill the gaps.

**light   frequency   electromagnetic
gamma   wavelength   radio**

The signals received by our radio and television sets are carried by .... waves. These belong to the family of .... waves which also includes light, microwaves and .... rays. All these waves travel at the speed of .... On a radio, the different stations may be identified by their .... (e.g. 198 m) or their .... (e.g. 97.3 MHz).

2 Copy and complete the table, filling in the blanks.

Type of radio wave	Properties	Uses
long wave (wavelength about 2000 m)	can follow the curvature of the Earth	.... broadcasts and .... communication
.... wave	can be reflected from ionosphere and bounced back to Earth using sky-wave propagation	used for radio broadcasting
microwaves	travel in straight lines through the ionosphere	used for............... communication

3 Draw a diagram to explain sky-wave propagation of radio waves. Show in your diagram how the wave is bounced off the ionosphere as it travels from the transmitter to the receiver.

4 A communications satellite orbits the Earth 35 000 km above the surface of the Earth. How long will it take for a radio signal to travel from the ground up to the satellite? (The velocity of electromagnetic waves is 300 000 km/s.)

5 The person in the diagram can listen to their radio, even though they cannot see the aerial transmitting the radio waves. Suggest two possible explanations for this.

radio transmitter

6 Winston sits watching an athletics event on television. The TV signal travels via satellite a total distance of 73 500 km. Winston hears the official fire the starting gun at exactly the same time as Joan, who is sitting 85 m from the gun at the athletics ground. Take the velocity of sound as 340 m/s, and the velocity of electromagnetic waves as 300 000 km/s.

a How far from his television set is Winston sitting?
b What assumptions have you made in answering this question?

8 Radiation in the home

1 Copy and complete these sentences, choosing the correct ending in each case.

a Infra-red radiation is....
b Microwave radiation with the correct wavelength can be....
c A sun tan is....
d A brightening agent may be....

Choose the endings from:
• ....used in washing powders and toothpastes.
• ....emitted by any hot object.
• ....used to cook food.
• ....produced as a result of exposure of the skin to ultra-violet radiation.

2 Microwave ovens are designed with special safety features so that microwave radiation cannot get out of the oven when it is switched on. Explain why this is necessary for the safety of the person using the oven. (Hint: think how the oven cooks food.)

3 When someone stands under a 'light' which gives off ultra-violet radiation at a party or a disco, their clothes may glow. Explain why.

4 The picture shows a rescue worker using thermal imaging equipment to help rescue people from a collapsed block of flats. Explain how equipment like this enables rescuers to detect people buried under rubble.

5 The 'protection factor' of a sunscreen is a guide to how much protection it can give you against ultra-violet radiation. For example, 'Factor 6' sunscreen will allow someone to stay out in the Sun roughly six times longer than they could if they were not wearing any sunscreen at all.

a Copy and complete the following table.

Sunscreen worn	Maximum safe time in Sun (mins)
None	15
Factor 2	i
Factor 6	ii
Factor 15	iii
Factor 24	iv

b In practice, it may not be safe to stay out in the Sun for as long as these times indicate. Why not?

6 The diagram shows a greenhouse, with the Sun shining on it. Radiation with wavelengths close to the wavelengths of visible light can pass through glass. Radiation with wavelengths much longer or shorter than this is reflected.

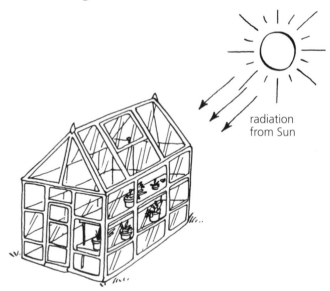

radiation from Sun

a Some radiation from the Sun will pass into the greenhouse. What effect will this have on the temperature of things inside the greenhouse? Explain your answer.
b Things inside the greenhouse emit infra-red radiation with a wavelength much longer than that of visible light. What will happen when this radiation reaches the glass in the greenhouse?
c Use your answers to parts **a** and **b** to explain how an unheated greenhouse works.

1 Copy and complete the following sentences, choosing the correct ending in each case.

a Cosmic radiation.....
b Radon and thoron.....
c Coal.....
d Radioactivity.....
e Natural radioactive material.....

Choose the endings from:
• .....are two radioactive gases found in the air.
• .....is taken up by plants and animals which may be eaten by humans.
• .....comes from space.
• .....contains small amounts of radioactive materials such as uranium and radium.
• .....may be detected using a Geiger counter.

2 Explain the following.

a Radioactivity is present inside your body as well as outside it.
b A regular air traveller receives a higher dose of radiation than someone who does not travel by air.
c Where you live may affect the radiation dose you receive.

3 The diagram shows the sources of the average radiation dose received in 1 year by someone living in the UK.

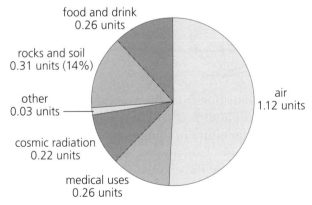

a Copy the pie chart, and add the percentages of the total radiation does for each source. (The percentage for 'rocks and soil' has been done for you.)
b What is the total average dose of radiation received?

c The source labelled 'other' includes radiation from nuclear weapon testing, from the Chernobyl accident, and from industrial uses of radiation. How does the dose from these sources compare to the dose from medical uses such as X-rays?
d Someone living in an area where the radiation from rocks is higher might receive a dose from this source of 0.5 units per year. Redraw the pie chart to show the dose that this person receives from all sources in 1 year.

4 The diagram shows how levels of radon gas in the air vary in different parts of the UK and Ireland.

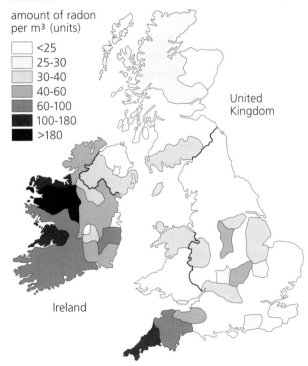

a Suggest why the levels are different in different parts of the country.
b Radon is likely to be a problem in homes that are poorly ventilated and which are located in parts of the country where radon levels are naturally high. Suggest some ways in which homes could be modified to reduce radon levels inside them.

1 Copy and complete the following sentences. Use the words below to fill the gaps (some words are used more than once).

alpha particles penetrating gamma electromagnetic beta

There are three main types of radiation given out by radioactive materials. These are called .... (α), ... (β) and .... (γ) radiation. Alpha and beta radiation consist of different types of .... Gamma radiation is .... radiation. The three different types of radiation have different .... powers: .... radiation is the most .... and .... radiation the least.

2 Copy the diagram and show on it the effect that smoke will have when it enters the detector. Explain how this switches the alarm on.

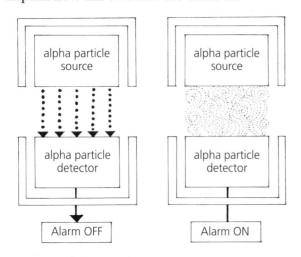

3 A person stands in front of a photographic film. A beam of X-rays is directed at them. Explain the following.

a The film shows the person's skeleton in white against a black background.
b The person must take off any metal objects such as brooches or pendants before having the X-ray.
c The person's exposure to X-rays should be kept to a minimum.

4 Copy and complete the diagram to show the penetrating power of alpha, beta and gamma radiation.

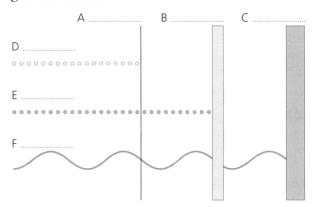

Use the labels below on your diagram.
- alpha radiation
- lead
- beta radiation
- aluminium
- gamma radiation
- paper

5 The diagram shows packets of tea passing along a conveyer belt. As the belt moves along, the packets pass through the beam of beta particles.

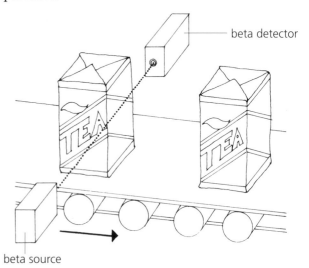

a Explain how this set-up can be used to count the packets of tea passing along the belt.
b Explain how this set-up also provides a way of indicating if a packet is not filled up to the top.

1 Copy and complete the table to show the likely effect of increasing doses of radiation.

Dose received	Effect
2.5 units	
1 000 units	
10 000 units	

2 Radon-220 has a half-life of 54 s. How much of a 20 g sample of this gas would remain after **a** 54 s **b** 108 s **c** 162 s **d** 1080 s?

3 Substances which emit gamma radiation can be used to obtain information about a patient's health. The patient is given a radioactive substance which emits gamma radiation. As the substance is absorbed by the part of the body under investigation (for example, the kidneys), a gamma camera is used to measure the gamma radiation coming from the body. This may produce a graph like that shown below.

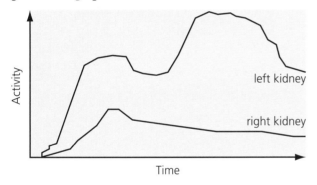

a Why are substances that emit gamma radiation used for diagnosis rather than substances which emit alpha radiation?
b What does the graph tell you about the behaviour of the patient's kidneys?

c The radioactive substance normally used to produce gamma rays inside a patient is an isotope of technetium, with a half-life of 6 hours. Why is this isotope used in preference to one with a much longer or shorter half-life?

4 Use the graph to answer the following questions.

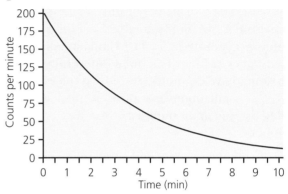

a Calculate the half-life of the substance.
b Calculate the count rate after
 i 1 half-life **ii** 2 half-lives **iii** 5 half-lives.
c How much of a 10 g sample of this substance would be left after 10 minutes?

5 Here is a statement about the nuclear accident which took place at the Chernobyl power station in the former Soviet Union in 1986.
- 'It will never be possible to tell how many people have died as a result of the accident at Chernobyl.'

Use the figures in the table at the bottom of the page to examine the statement critically. Do you agree or disagree with the statement? Consider:
- can you be sure about the data in the table?
- how sure can you be that someone has died as a *direct* result of the Chernobyl accident?
- how do you decide what is an acceptable risk and what is not? Who makes this decision?

Table for **Q5**

	Western former Soviet Union	UK	Rest of Europe
Population at time of accident	75 000 000	56 000 000	400 000 000
Estimated total deaths 1986 – 2026	30 000 000	26 000 000	160 000 000
Estimated cancer deaths 1986 – 2026	6 000 000	6 000 000	35 000 000
Estimated cancer deaths due to background radiation 1986 – 2026	78 000	40 000	416 000
Deaths due to Chernobyl	8 000 to 34 000	40	2 000

1 Copy and complete the following sentences. Use the words below to fill the gaps (some words are used more than once).

neutrons element nucleus protons atomic electrons

The atom is made up of three basic particles: .... , ... and .... At the centre of the atom is the .... which contains the .... and .... The number of protons in an atom is always equal to the number of .... All atoms which have the same number of protons belong to the same .... The number of protons in an atom is called the .... number or the .... number.

2 Copy and complete the table.

Particle in the atom	Mass	Charge
proton		
neutron		
electron		

3 The element sodium has an atomic number of 11. Its isotopes have mass numbers of 22, 23 and 24. The diagram shows a sodium atom with mass number 23. Draw similar diagrams for the other two isotopes.

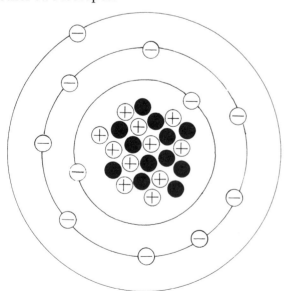

4 Copy and complete the table to show the number of protons, neutrons and electrons in each atom. Use this information to identify the element to which each atom belongs.

● = neutron ○ = proton • = electron	Atomic number	Mass number	Element
	a	b	c
	d	e	boron
	f	g	h
	i	j	oxygen
k	8	18	l

5 Copy and complete the following table. Draw diagrams to describe the radioactive decays in the table.

Starting atom	Decay	Final atom
mass no. = 32 atomic no. = 15	beta	a
b	alpha	mass no. = 234 atomic no. = 90
mass no. = 232 atomic no. = 90	c	mass no. = 228 atomic no. = 88

1 The waves associated with an earthquake are of two types – P and S. P waves and S waves travel differently, in the same way that sound waves and water waves travel differently.

a Describe the difference between P waves and S waves, using words and diagrams.

b The P waves from an earthquake are always registered before the S waves. Why is this?

The drawing shows an earthquake detector designed by the Chinese scientist Chung Heng in about AD130. As earthquake waves reach the detector, the pendulum swings and the balls fall from the mouth of the dragon into the mouths of the waiting frogs.

pendulum

c Would this detector detect P waves and S waves equally well? Explain your answer.

2 The table shows the thickness of the layers making up the Earth (including the atmosphere).

Layer	Thickness	Structure
atmosphere	1100 km	
crust	30 km	
mantle	2900 km	
outer core	2200 km	
inner core	1270 km	

a Copy and complete the table, describing the structure of each layer as thoroughly as you can.

b Draw a diagram to show these layers to scale, as far as you can.

3 The diagram shows waves from an earthquake spreading out through the Earth.

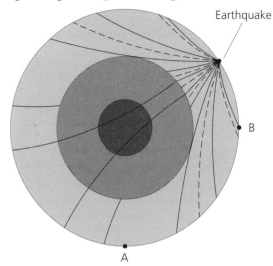

a Copy and complete the diagram to show the waves passing through the outer and inner cores.

b What would be registered by a seismograph sited at A? Explain your answer.

c What would be registered by a seismograph sited at B? Explain your answer.

4 The graph shows how the velocity of seismic waves varies with depth below the surface of the Earth.

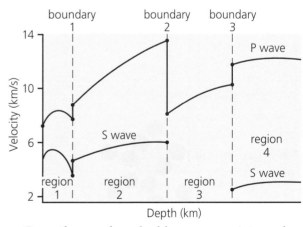

a Copy the graph and add an appropriate scale to the x-axis.

b Explain why there are *two* lines on the graph.

c Explain why the graph shows sharp changes in velocity in certain places.

d Explain why the lines on the graph are curved in some places and straight in others.

e Why is there no line for the S wave in region 3?

1 Match each type of electromagnetic radiation with one of its uses and then copy them out.

- **X-rays**
- **Radio waves**
- **Infra-red waves**
- **Light waves**
- **Gamma waves**
- **Ultra-violet waves**
- **Microwaves**

cook food under a grill

are visible to the eye

can be used to see inside a person's body

have wavelengths longer than about 10 cm

help to produce a sun tan

cook food by transferring energy to water molecules

are given off by some radioactive substances

2 Copy the diagram of the electromagnetic spectrum. Use the labels below on your diagram, to show how the radiation can be detected.

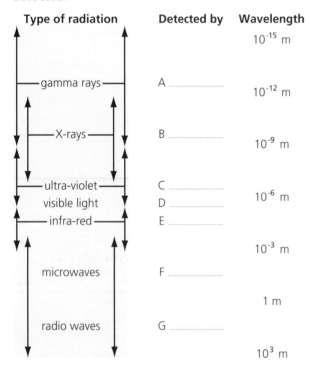

Type of radiation	Detected by	Wavelength
		10^{-15} m
gamma rays	A	10^{-12} m
X-rays	B	10^{-9} m
ultra-violet	C	
visible light	D	10^{-6} m
infra-red	E	
		10^{-3} m
microwaves	F	
		1 m
radio waves	G	
		10^{3} m

- Geiger counter
- photographic film
- skin (sunburn)
- eye
- skin (heat)
- water molecules
- electrical circuits

3 **a** Copy and complete the diagrams showing the behaviour of water waves passing through a gap.

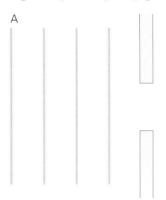

A

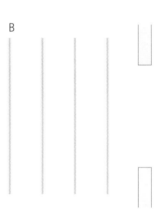

B

b What is the name given to this kind of behaviour?

4 Some teachers claim to be able to see round corners! Explain why it is possible to hear round corners when it is not possible to see round them.

Data

Periodic Table

| I | II | | | | | | | | | | | | | III | IV | V | VI | VII | O |

Example: gold
relative atomic mass (A_r) $^{197}_{79}$Au
atomic number (Z)

Alkali Metals

Noble Gases

Halogens

$^{1}_{1}$H

$^{4}_{2}$He

1

2 $^{7}_{3}$Li $^{9}_{4}$Be   Transition Metals $^{11}_{5}$B $^{12}_{6}$C $^{14}_{7}$N $^{16}_{8}$O $^{19}_{9}$F $^{20}_{10}$Ne

3 $^{23}_{11}$Na $^{24}_{12}$Mg $^{27}_{13}$Al $^{28}_{14}$Si $^{31}_{15}$P $^{32}_{16}$S $^{35.5}_{17}$Cl $^{40}_{18}$Ar

4 $^{39}_{19}$K $^{40}_{20}$Ca $^{45}_{21}$Sc $^{48}_{22}$Ti $^{51}_{23}$V $^{52}_{24}$Cr $^{55}_{25}$Mn $^{56}_{26}$Fe $^{59}_{27}$Co $^{59}_{28}$Ni $^{64}_{29}$Cu $^{65}_{30}$Zn $^{70}_{31}$Ga $^{73}_{32}$Ge $^{75}_{33}$As $^{79}_{34}$Se $^{80}_{35}$Br $^{84}_{36}$Kr

5 $^{85.5}_{37}$Rb $^{88}_{38}$Sr $^{89}_{39}$Y $^{91}_{40}$Zr $^{93}_{41}$Nb $^{96}_{42}$Mo $^{99}_{43}$Tc $^{101}_{44}$Ru $^{103}_{45}$Rh $^{106}_{46}$Pd $^{108}_{47}$Ag $^{112}_{48}$Cd $^{115}_{49}$In $^{119}_{50}$Sn $^{122}_{51}$Sb $^{128}_{52}$Te $^{127}_{53}$I $^{131}_{54}$Xe

6 $^{133}_{55}$Cs $^{137}_{56}$Ba $^{139}_{57}$La $^{178.5}_{72}$Hf $^{181}_{73}$Ta $^{184}_{74}$W $^{186}_{75}$Re $^{190}_{76}$Os $^{192}_{77}$Ir $^{195}_{78}$Pt $^{197}_{79}$Au $^{201}_{80}$Hg $^{204}_{81}$Tl $^{207}_{82}$Pb $^{209}_{83}$Bi $^{209}_{84}$Po $^{210}_{85}$At $^{222}_{86}$Rn

7 $^{223}_{87}$Fr $^{226}_{88}$Ra $^{227}_{89}$Ac

Relative atomic masses of selected elements

Element	Symbol	Relative atomic mass (A_r)
aluminium	Al	27
bromine	Br	80
carbon	C	12
chlorine	Cl	35.5
copper	Cu	64
fluorine	F	19
hydrogen	H	1
iron	Fe	56
magnesium	Mg	24
nitrogen	N	14
oxygen	O	16
phosphorus	P	31
potassium	K	39
sodium	Na	23
sulphur	S	32
vanadium	V	51

Reactivity series of selected elements

potassium	most reactive
sodium	
calcium	
magnesium	
aluminium	
carbon	
zinc	
iron	
lead	
hydrogen	
copper	
silver	
gold	
platinum	least reactive

Melting points of selected metals (°C)

aluminium	660
copper	1083
gold	1064
iron	1540
magnesium	640
mercury	-39
silver	960
titanium	1660

acceleration rate at which the velocity of an object changes with time.

acid solution with a pH less than 7.

acid rain rain polluted with acidic gases such as sulphur dioxide; the gases come from burning fossil fuels.

activation energy energy which must be supplied to reactants before they will react.

active uptake uptake of ions against a concentration gradient; involves the use of energy.

adaptation the features of an organism which help it live in its environment.

ADH (antidiuretic hormone) hormone from the pituitary gland involved in water balance in the kidneys.

aerobic respiration breaking down glucose in the presence of oxygen.

air pollution pollution of the air (*see* pollution).

alcohol the legal addictive drug in alcoholic drinks.

alkali solution with a pH greater than 7.

alkali metals Group I of the Periodic Table; soft, very reactive metals such as sodium and potassium.

alkanes family of hydrocarbons that have single bonds only between their carbon atoms.

alkenes family of hydrocarbons that contain (at least) one carbon to carbon double bond.

alleles genes which occur in different forms.

alloy homogeneous mixture of two or more metals.

alpha radiation weakly penetrating radiation produced by certain radioactive substances.

alternating current (a.c.) electric current which flows backwards and forwards, such as mains electricity.

alveoli tiny air sacs in the lungs where gas exchange takes place.

amino acids the basic units of proteins.

ammeter instrument used to measure electric current.

ampere (A) unit of electric current.

amplitude maximum height of a wave.

anaerobic respiration breaking down glucose without oxygen.

anode positive electrode.

antibodies chemicals made by white blood cells which destroy microbes.

antitoxins chemicals made by white blood cells which counteract the poisons (toxins) made by microbes.

artery blood vessel carrying blood away from the heart.

artificial insemination inserting semen from a selected male into a female without natural mating.

artificial selection producing new varieties of animals and plants by breeding from selected parents.

asexual reproduction reproduction involving only one parent, producing genetically identical offspring.

astronomical unit (AU) unit of distance; 1 AU = 150 million km.

atmosphere blanket of air around the Earth.

atom smallest particle of an element.

atomic number (Z) number of protons in the nucleus of an element; also called the proton number. All atoms of the same element have the same atomic number.

auxin plant hormone, important in growth and plant responses.

background radiation radiation from all around us and within us.

bacteria microorganisms, some of which are harmful and cause disease, others of which are helpful.

balanced forces when the forces acting on an object cancel each other out; they do not affect the movement of the object they are acting on.

bauxite ore of aluminium, more common than cryolite.

beta radiation moderately penetrating radiation produced by certain radioactive substances.

Big Bang massive explosion in which astronomers believe the Universe was created 15 000 million years ago.

biological washing powder washing powder containing enzymes to help get clothes cleaner at low temperatures.

bioreactors large industrial fermenters for making products using bacteria.

black hole massive star which has collapsed, with a gravitational field around it so large that nothing, not even light, can escape from it.

blast furnace used for making iron from iron ore, using limestone and coke.

blood mixture of cells and chemicals which acts as transport medium for the body.

bronchi two tubes branching off from trachea.

bronchioles small tubes branching into lungs.

cancer uncontrolled development of cells in the body.

capillary very tiny blood vessel carrying blood close to the cells.

carbohydrase carbohydrate-digesting enzyme.

carbohydrate food type, used by the body as a source of energy.

carbon cycle the cycling of carbon through living organisms and the environment.

carbon dioxide waste gas produced in respiration or from burning fuels.

carnivore an organism which feeds on animals.

catalyst substance that increases the rate of a reaction without altering anything else; it is not used up during the reaction and can be used over and over again.

cathode negative electrode.

cell basic building block of living organisms.

cell division process by which cells divide in growth and reproduction.

cell membrane controls passage of chemicals in and out of the cell.

cell wall wall made of cellulose surrounding and strengthening plant cells.

cellulose complex carbohydrate used for plant cell walls.

central nervous system controls and coordinates the nervous system; consists of the brain and spinal cord.

chain reaction self-sustaining nuclear reaction in which atoms fission and expel particles that split other atoms; if uncontrolled can lead to a nuclear explosion.

chemical energy energy stored in chemicals such as fuels.

chemical reaction when two or more substances combine to make one or more new substances; in general, not easily reversible.

chlorophyll green pigment which absorbs energy from sunlight.

chloroplasts packets of the green pigment chlorophyll found in some plant cells; where photosynthesis takes place.

cholera bacterial disease spread by poor hygiene.

chromosome carries information in the form of genes which control the characteristics of an individual.

cilia hair-like projections from cells.

circulatory system network of blood vessels carrying blood around the body.

clone offspring produced in asexual reproduction.

clots solid material formed by blood to seal cuts.

combustion reaction between a fuel and oxygen that gives out heat energy and produces a flame; burning.

community all the organisms living in a particular habitat.

competition organisms struggling against each other for the same thing.

compound substance made from two or more different elements chemically joined together.

condensation when a gas cools and turns back to a liquid.

conductor (electrical) something which allows electricity to flow freely.

conductor (heat) something which allows heat to flow freely.

constellation pattern of stars in the sky, which may be given names like 'The Plough' or 'The Hunter'.

consumer organism (usually an animal) which cannot make its own food and so eats other organisms.

contraceptive drugs hormones which can be used to prevent the release of eggs from the ovary and so prevent pregnancy.

convection the way heat energy is transferred in liquids and gases; hot material rises and cool material sinks.

core body temperature internal body temperature; about 37 °C for humans.

cosmic radiation radiation from space.

coulomb unit of electrical charge.

covalent bond chemical bond formed by sharing electrons between atoms.

critical angle angle of the incident ray at which the refracted ray is refracted at 90° to the normal.

crumple zone part of a car body which deforms permanently when it is hit in an accident, absorbing the energy of the impact.

crust thin solid layer at the surface of the Earth.

crustal plates the crust of the Earth is broken up into moving slabs called plates.

cryolite ore of aluminium, less common than bauxite.

cumulative poison poison which builds up slowly in the body from repeated exposures.

current electricity flow of electrical charge.

cuttings new plants formed from small parts of an older plant.

cystic fibrosis a relatively common inherited disorder which affects the lungs and gut; recessive.

cytoplasm jelly-like material where most of the chemical reactions of the cell take place.

DDT an insecticide which is passed along the food chain.

decay curve plot of the radioactivity of a substance against time.

decomposers organisms which break down dead animals and plants and recycle the nutrients.

deforestation destroying forests.

ΔH energy released or absorbed during a reaction; if ΔH is negative, energy is released; if ΔH is positive, energy is absorbed.

detritus feeders organisms which feed on dead bodies and waste products.

diabetes condition caused when the pancreas does not make enough insulin.

diffraction waves spreading out as they pass through a gap which is about the same size as their wavelength.

diffusion liquids and gases mix and spread naturally by diffusion as the particles move around and collide with each other.

digestive system group of organs carrying out digestion and absorption of food.

diode special type of resistor which allows electricity to flow in one direction only.

direct current (d.c.) electric current which only flows in one direction, such as the current from a battery.

displacement reaction reaction in which one substance replaces another.

dissolving solid particles break up and mix in with those of a liquid; the solid seems to disappear, but you can get it back again.

distance–time graph graph plotted to show the distance something has travelled against time.

DNA chemical which contains the coded information for life.

dominant allele characteristic always shows, even if only one allele is present.

drag force force which acts on an object moving through a fluid; always acts in the opposite direction to the direction in which the object is moving.

drug a chemical which changes the way the body works.

egg female animal sex cell.

elastic limit if an object (e.g. a spring) is stretched beyond its elastic limit, it does not return to its original length when the force stretching it is removed; it is permanently deformed.

elastic potential energy energy stored in an object that has been changed in shape without going beyond its elastic limit.

electrode electric terminal used in electrolysis.

electrolysis breaking up chemical compounds using electricity when molten or in solution in water.

electrolytes ionic liquids that conduct electricity.

electrolytic refining method of purifying copper and some other metals using electricity.

electromagnet magnet made by the flow of electricity through a coil; it can be switched on and off.

electron tiny, negatively charged particle found in atoms; current electricity is a flow of electrons.

electron shell possible electron positions around a nucleus; sometimes called energy levels.

element substances that cannot be broken down into simpler substances; for example, carbon and oxygen. Elements are made from one kind of atom only.

Elodea pond weed used in photosynthesis experiments.

embryo transplants transferring embryos from one animal to another.

endoscope instrument made of optical fibres, used by doctors to look inside the body.

endothermic reaction reaction which absorbs energy.

energy has many different forms – heat, light, sound, electrical, kinetic, potential, chemical; needed to carry out actions of life.

energy level *see* electron shell.

environmental factors factors in your way of life which affect how you turn out.

enzyme protein molecule which changes the rate of a chemical reaction in the body – biological catalyst.

epidermis transparent, protective outer layer of leaf.

equilibrium when the rate of a reversible reaction is exactly the same in both directions.

equilibrium mixture mixture of products and reactants that is present when a reversible reaction reaches equilibrium.

eutrophication the death of most living organisms in a river as a result of excess nitrate fertiliser in the river.

evolution the development of life forms on Earth by small changes over a very long period of time.

excretion removing the waste products of the chemical reactions which go on in the body.

exothermic reaction reaction which releases energy.

extension the amount something (e.g. a spring) has stretched; calculated using the formula
*extension = length when force applied –
length when no force applied*

extinct no longer found alive on Earth.

eye sense organ responding to light.

family tree way of showing how a characteristic is passed on through the generations.

fat food type, used by body for energy and as an energy store.

fermentation conversion of sugar to alcohol and carbon dioxide.

fertilisation the fusing of the male and female gametes.

fertiliser substance added to the soil to replace nutrients taken out by plants; often put on soils to increase crop growth.

fertility drugs hormones which can be used to stimulate the release of eggs from the ovary.

fluorescence when a substance absorbs ultra-violet radiation and re-emits the energy as visible light.

food chain a way of linking organisms to show the feeding relationships between them.

food web a more complex way of linking organisms to show the feeding inter-relationships.

force a push or a pull (*see also* balanced forces and unbalanced forces).

fossil fuels fuels made from the remains of living things over millions of years; coal, oil and gas.

fossils shells or bones of dead organisms from millions of years ago found in sedimentary rock.

fractionating column cooling tower in which vaporised crude oil (a mixture of hydrocarbons) is allowed to cool, the different hydrocarbons condensing at different temperatures and so are separated.

frequency number of waves produced by a source in one second.

frictional forces forces produced when solid surfaces rub together, or when an object moves through a fluid such as air or water; often slow down movement.

froth flotation method of separating ore from rock using water containing detergent through which air is blown.

FSH follicle-stimulating hormone.

galaxy cluster or group of billions of stars.

gall bladder stores bile for release into small intestine.

gamete sex cell (either sperm or egg).

gamma radiation strongly penetrating radiation produced by certain radioactive substances.

gaseous exchange the exchange of oxygen and carbon dioxide which takes place in the alveoli.

generator device which turns motion (kinetic energy) into electrical energy.

gene therapy transferring healthy genes to the cells of individuals who have inherited faulty ones.

genes make up chromosomes; they carry instructions for making proteins.

genetic engineering transferring genes from one organism to another.

geostationary orbit a satellite in a geostationary orbit above the Earth's equator orbits the Earth once every 24 hours; because of this, it is always above the same point on the Earth's surface.

geothermal energy heat energy taken from hot rocks below the surface of the Earth.

giant molecules materials such as diamond where all the atoms are held together by strong covalent bonds; they are hard and have high melting points.

glucagon hormone involved in controlling blood sugar levels.

glucose the main food used in respiration to provide energy.

gravitational potential energy energy stored in something that has been lifted up against gravity.

gravity/gravitational force force which attracts two masses to each other; the force that pulls things to the Earth.

greenhouse effect gradual warming of the Earth's surface as a result of a build-up of gases such as carbon dioxide and methane.

ground-wave propagation radiowaves following the curvature of the Earth.

growth making new cells.

growth hormone hormone needed for normal growth to occur.

guard cells open and close stomata.

gut digestive tract from mouth to anus.

Haber process used to make ammonia from nitrogen and hydrogen.

habitat the place where an animal or plant lives.

haemoglobin pigment found in red blood cells which carries oxygen.

half-life time taken for the radioactivity of a substance to fall by half.

halogens Group VII of the Periodic Table; very reactive non-metals such as chlorine and bromine.

hazard symbol symbol used to identify the hazards associated with particular chemicals.

heart muscular double pump, pumping blood to lungs and around the body.

heat conduction the way heat energy is moved through solids such as metals.

heat radiation the transfer of heat energy as infra-red waves similar to light.

herbivore an organism which feeds on plants.

heterozygous the chromosomes in a pair contain different alleles.

homeostasis keeping conditions constant in the body.

homozygous both chromosomes in a pair contain the same allele.

hormone chemicals released in one part of the body and carried in the blood to have an effect somewhere else.

Huntington's chorea a rare inherited disorder which affects the nervous system; dominant.

hydrocarbon molecule made from carbon and hydrogen atoms only.

hydroelectric power electrical power generated by falling water.

hypothermia condition when core body temperature becomes too low.

identical twins twins which develop from a single fertilised egg cell and are genetically identical.

igneous rock rock formed when molten rock (magma) cools and hardens.

illegal drugs drugs which it is against the law to possess or use.

immune being resistant to a disease which you have met before.

immunisation *see* vaccination.

incident ray light ray before it is reflected or refracted.

indicator substance used to show whether a solution is acid or alkali.

influenza viral disease spread by droplets in the air.

infra-red electromagnetic radiation given off by any warm object; it has a wavelength longer than the wavelength of visible light.

inherited characteristics features passed on from one generation to the next.

inherited disorder disease which is passed on as a result of faulty genes.

inner core solid layer at the centre of the Earth.

insulator (electrical) something through which electricity is unable to flow.

insulator (heat) something through which heat energy is unable to flow.

insulin hormone involved in controlling blood sugar levels.

ion atom or group of atoms which have lost or gained one or more electrons, becoming charged.

ionic bond chemical bond formed between oppositely charged ions, such as metals (+ve) and non-metals (−ve).

ionic substance made up of a combination of positive and negative ions.

ionising radiation radiation which produces ions when it travels through matter.

isotopes different versions of the same element; that is, they have the same atomic number, but different mass numbers (due to a different number of neutrons in the nucleus).

joule (J) unit of energy.

Kepler's laws three laws concerned with the orbits of the planets around the Sun.

kidneys organs which remove urea, excess water and salt from the blood to form urine.

kilowatt hour (kWh) large unit of energy, used to measure how much electricity has been used in the home.

kinetic energy energy which a moving object has; calculated using the formula
kinetic energy (J) = ½ x *mass (kg)* x
(velocity (m/s))²

lactic acid waste product produced in anaerobic respiration.

large intestine last part of gut where water is absorbed and faeces stored.

leaves plant organs adapted for photosynthesis.

lens part of the eye which helps focus light.

LH luteinising hormone.

life processes seven processes which every living organism carries out (movement, respiration, growth, reproduction, excretion, sensitivity and feeding).

lipase fat-digesting enzyme.

litmus indicator; in acid solutions litmus is red, in alkaline solutions it is blue.

live wire mains electricity wire that carries the alternating voltage that drives the current.

liver produces bile, detoxifies chemicals, etc.

Local Group the Milky Way is part of a group of about 20 galaxies which astronomers call the Local Group, e.g. sound waves.

longitudinal wave wave in which the vibrations occur in the same direction as the wave travels.

lungs organs of gas exchange in the chest.

macronutrients main nutrients needed by plants.

magma molten rock.

main sequence star star in the main, stable period of its life.

malnutrition not eating the right food to remain healthy.

mantle hot, soft rocky middle layer of the Earth, between the core and the crust.

mass measure of the amount of matter in a body; wherever an object is, its mass is always the same.

mass number (A) the mass of an atom relative to hydrogen (= 1); the total number of nucleons (protons and neutrons) in the nucleus. (*See* relative atomic mass.)

meiosis cell division which results in a halving of the numbers of chromosomes; involved in gamete formation only.

menstrual cycle cycle of fertility in women controlled by hormones.

metal shiny substance that conducts electricity; all metals, except mercury, are solid at room temperature.

metamorphic rock rock formed when other rocks are heated and/or squashed without melting.

methane a hydrocarbon produced when vegetation rots under water and also contained in waste gases from animals like cows and sheep.

microwaves electromagnetic radiation with a wavelength longer than that of infra-red radiation; they can be used for radio and telephone communication and for cooking food.

Milky Way galaxy in which our solar system is found.

mineral ions needed in minute quantities for healthy growth in animals and plants.

mitosis cell division which results in identical cells with identical copies of the chromosomes.

mole amount of substance containing 6.02×10^{23} particles.

molecule group of atoms joined together by chemical bonds; has no charge.

motor neurones carry messages from the CNS to the muscles in the body.

mutation a sudden change in the genetic material.

natural selection organisms best suited to an environment are most likely to survive and reproduce, passing on their genes.

net energy transfer energy released or absorbed during a reaction.

neurone nerve cell.

neutral a solution with a pH of exactly 7.

neutralisation reaction between an acid and a base to produce one or more neutral substances.

neutron uncharged particle found in the nucleus of an atom.

neutron star remains of a star which has exploded in a supernova, leaving behind enormously dense matter.

newton (N) unit of force.

nicotine the legal addictive drug in cigarettes.

nitrates source of nitrogen from the soil needed for protein formation and healthy plant growth.

nitrogen cycle the cycling of nitrogen through living organisms and the environment.

noble gases Group VIII (or 0) of the Periodic Table; totally unreactive gases such as helium and argon.

non-metals most non-metal elements have low melting and boiling points, and do not conduct electricity.

non-renewable energy sources fossil fuels which will run out and cannot be replaced.

normal line at right angles to a surface; in reflection a normal ray will be reflected back along its own path and in refraction a normal ray is not bent when it travels from one material into another.

nuclear energy energy produced from radioactivity.

nuclear fission splitting of a heavy nucleus to produce two lighter elements and energy; a radioactive process.

nucleon particles (protons and neutrons) found in the nucleus of an atom.

nucleon number *see* mass number.

nucleus (atom) central part of an atom, that carries most of the mass and has a positive charge.

nucleus (cell) contains genetic material and controls the activities of the cell.

oestrogen hormone which stimulates the building up of the lining of the uterus ready for pregnancy.

ohm (Ω) unit of electrical resistance.

optic nerve carries messages from the retina to the brain.

optical fibre thin flexible rod of glass; light travels along the fibre due to total internal reflection.

organ group of tissues working together to carry out a particular job (e.g. heart).

organ system collection of organs carrying out related functions (e.g. circulatory system).

oscilloscope instrument that can be used with a microphone to enable sound waves to be 'seen' on a screen.

osmosis movement of water along a concentration gradient through a partially permeable membrane.

outer core liquid layer of the Earth which lies around the inner core; made of iron and nickel.

ovary organ producing eggs and hormones in the female.

oviduct tube connecting the ovary to the uterus.

oxygen gas in air needed for respiration.

oxyhaemoglobin haemoglobin combined with oxygen.

oxidation removal of electrons from a substance, often by a reaction with oxygen; the opposite of reduction.

ozone layer layer of a special form of oxygen high in the atmosphere which protects the Earth from harmful rays from the Sun.

P waves longitudinal seismic (earthquake) waves.

palisade cells close-packed cells at top of leaf containing many chloroplasts.

parallel circuit electrical circuit with two (or more) loops.

partially permeable membrane membrane which only allows particles below a certain size to pass through it.

Periodic Table a way of ordering the elements to show natural families with similar properties.

peristalsis muscular squeezing of gut which moves food along gut.

permanent magnet magnet made from steel or iron that cannot have its magnetism 'switched off'.

phenolphthalein an indicator; in acid solutions it is clear, in alkaline solutions it is pink.

phloem transport tissue made of living cells which moves food around plant (compare with xylem).

photosynthesis process by which plants use energy from sunlight to make their own food from carbon dioxide and water; takes place in chloroplasts.

pig iron iron straight from the blast furnace, containing about 95% iron, the rest being mainly carbon.

pituitary gland gland in the brain which produces a number of hormones.

planet body orbiting a star; larger than comets and asteroids.

plasma liquid part of blood.

plate tectonics movement of the Earth's crustal plates, which can open oceans or build mountains.

platelets fragments of cells involved in the clotting mechanism.

pollution things which are added to the environment which are harmful to life.

polymerisation reaction when small molecules join up to form very long chain molecules, e.g. polythene, nylon.

population group of organisms of the same species living in the same area.

predator animal which kills and eats other animals.

pressure force acting over a given area; calculated using the formula
pressure (Pa) = force (N)/area (m²)

prey animals which are caught and eaten by predators.

primary consumer organism which feeds on producers.

producer organism which can make its own food by photosynthesis; usually a plant.

products new substances formed during a chemical reaction.

propagator special enclosed space to keep cuttings damp and warm as they grow.

protease protein-digesting enzyme.

protein food type, used by the body as raw material for growth.

proton positively charged particle found in the nucleus of an atom.

proton number *see* atomic number.

protostar beginnings of a star, formed when a cloud of gas and dust collapses under its own gravitational field.

pulse pressure wave from contraction of heart felt at points such as wrist and neck.

pyramid of biomass the amount of living material at each level of a food chain, represented as a pyramid.

pyramid of numbers the number of organisms at each level in a food chain, represented as a pyramid.

radiation energy spreading out from a source.

radioactive decay when a radioactive substance emits radiation.

radioactive fallout radiation from nuclear tests and nuclear accidents which escapes into the atmosphere.

radioactivity natural breakdown of unstable atoms that releases energy.

radioisotope radioactive isotope of an element.

radiowaves electromagnetic waves with a frequency lower than the frequency of microwaves.

reactants substances present at the start of a chemical reaction.

reaction rate speed of a reaction; the greater the reaction rate, the faster the reaction goes.

reactivity used to describe the chemical behaviour of a substance; reactive substances join up easily with other substances, unreactive substances do not.

reactivity series list showing substances in order of reactivity.

receptors special nerve cells which respond to a change in stimulus.

recessive allele characteristic only shows up if the allele is present in the homozygous state.

recycling movement of nutrients through living organisms, the air and/or the soil, to be used over and over again.

red blood cells cells which transport oxygen in the blood.

red giant star which has expanded as it begins to use up all its hydrogen.

red shift tendency for light coming from stars moving away from us very quickly to be shifted towards the red end of the spectrum.

reduction addition of electrons to a substance, often by the removal of oxygen; the opposite of oxidation.

reflected ray light ray after it has bounced off the surface of an object.

reflection waves which bounce off a solid surface are said to be reflected.

reflex action very rapid response to stimulus which does not involve conscious thought.

refracted ray light ray after it has changed direction of travel.

refraction waves may be bent when they move into an area where they travel at a different speed; this is called refraction.

relative atomic mass (A_r) mass of an atom compared to other atoms; A_r for hydrogen is 1 and A_r for carbon is 12, so a carbon atom is 12 times heavier than a hydrogen atom. *See* mass number.

relative formula mass (M_r) sum of all the relative atomic masses of the atoms making up a compound.

renewable energy sources energy sources which will not run out, such as solar power or geothermal energy.

resistance wire special wire which restricts the flow of electricity.

resistor an electrical component that restricts the flow of electricity.

respiration releases energy from food in a cell.

retina layer of light-sensitive cells at the back of the eye.

reversible reaction reaction that can go forwards and backwards.

roasting heating a metal ore in air.

root hair cell specialised root cell through which water is absorbed into the plant.

roots organs that anchor plants in ground, take up water and can store starch.

S waves transverse seismic (earthquake) waves.

salt substance formed when an acid and a base react together.

satellite small object orbiting a larger one.

saturated hydrocarbons hydrocarbons that have single carbon to carbon bonds only.

scanning ultrasound waves can be used to scan the inside of a person's body to produce a 'picture' of what is inside.

secondary consumer organism which feeds on primary or other consumers.

sedimentary rock rock made from the broken fragments of other rocks.

seed product of sexual reproduction in plants; contains the new embryo plant.

seismic waves waves from an explosion or earthquake spreading through the body of the Earth.

seismometer machine that records the vibrations from earthquakes.

sense organs sensitive to particular stimuli.

sensitivity responding to changes in the surroundings.

sensory neurones carry messages from receptors to the CNS.

series circuit electrical circuit with just one continuous loop.

sewage farm site where human waste is treated to prevent it damaging the environment.

sewer large pipe which carries waste water to the sewage works.

sex chromosome chromosomes which determine sex; in humans, the X and Y chromosomes.

sexual reproduction reproduction involving two parents and the fusing of gametes to produce genetically different offspring.

sickle cell anaemia an inherited disorder affecting the haemoglobin.

skin covering of the body, barrier to the entry of disease.

sky-wave propagation radiowaves bounced between the surface of the Earth and the upper atmosphere.

slag waste material produced in the blast furnace during the production of iron.

small intestine main area of gut for digestion and absorption of food.

sound wave vibrations set up in the air by a vibrating object.

speed the distance an object travels in a given time; a measure of how fast the object is travelling.

sperm male animal sex cell.

starch form in which energy is stored in plants.

static electricity build-up of electrical charge.

steel range of metals containing iron and other substances such as carbon, nickel and other elements.

stimulus change in the surroundings.

stomach stores and mixes food with enzymes and acid; part of digestive system.

stomata pores in the surface of plants through which gases and water vapour move.

stratigraphic column standard sequence of rocks of different ages; each age has different fossils.

supernova massive explosion in which matter from a star is flung far out into space.

synapse junction between two nerve cells.

terminal velocity speed at which there is no unbalanced force acting on a freely falling body.

thermoregulatory centre area of brain involved in control of body temperature.

tissue group of similar cells together performing a particular function.

tissue culture producing new plants from small clumps of cells taken from an older plant.

total internal reflection occurs when a ray strikes the side of a block of glass at an angle greater than the critical angle, so that the ray is reflected back into the block rather than travelling back out into the air.

toxins poisons produced by bacteria.

trachea the windpipe.

transformer electrical device which can change the voltage and current in a.c. circuits.

transition metals family of 'everyday' metals such as iron and copper that forms a block in the middle of the Periodic Table.

transpiration the loss of water by evaporation from the leaves of plants.

transverse wave wave in which the vibrations occur at right angles to the direction in which the wave travels, e.g. light waves.

turbine motor which is made to spin by water or steam pushing against fan blades.

turgor the pressure of cell sap against the plant cell wall which gives the plant support.

ultrasonic cleaning using ultrasound to clean objects.

ultrasound sound of very high frequency that cannot be heard by humans.

ultra-violet electromagnetic radiation that can give you a suntan; it has a wavelength shorter than the wavelength of visible light.

unbalanced forces when the forces acting on an object do not cancel each other out they are said to be unbalanced; they change the movement of an object, making it speed up, slow down, or change direction.

unsaturated hydrocarbons hydrocarbons that have at least one carbon to carbon double or triple bond.

urea the waste product of protein breakdown.

uterus (womb) organ which contains the developing baby during pregnancy.

vaccination (immunisation) exposing your body to dead or weakened microbes so the white blood cells produce antibodies which will protect you from catching the disease in the future.

vacuole permanent membrane-lined space in plant cells filled with cell sap.

vein blood vessel carrying blood towards the heart.

velocity speed of an object in a given direction.

velocity–time graph graph plotted to show the velocity of an object against time.

villi finger-like folds of the small intestine wall which increase the surface area.

virus microbes which cause disease.

visible spectrum white light split up into the colours of the rainbow.

voltage (V) unit of electrical potential; a measure of how much energy is carried by an electric current.

voltmeter instrument used to measure electric potential (voltage).

watt (W) unit of electrical power.

wave disturbance which carries energy.

wavelength distance between two nearest identical points on a wave.

weight force acting on an object in a gravitational field; calculated using the formula
weight (N) = mass (kg) × gravitational field strength (N/kg)

white blood cells help defend the body against disease.

white dwarf star at a late stage in its life which has collapsed under its own gravity.

womb *see* uterus.

work measure of energy transferred when a force moves; calculated using the formula
work (J) = force (N) × distance moved in direction of force (m)

X-rays electromagnetic radiation with a wavelength shorter than that of ultra-violet radiation; can be used to get a shadow picture of the bones in the body.

xylem transport tissue made of dead cells which moves water around plant (compare with phloem).

yield amount of product made in a chemical reaction; usually expressed as a percentage of the maximum possible amount of product(s) that can be made from a given quantity of starting materials.

Index